The Trees Went Forth

A NOVEL

by

WALTER O'ME

D1158789

CROWN PUBLISHERS   NEW YORK

INTRODUCTION TO 1982 PRINTING

The Trees Went Forth, a book about logging in northern Minnesota, was the first of an impressive list of historical novels by Walter O'Meara, which include *The Savage Country, The Last Portage* and *Minnesota Gothic.* In many cases, the subject matter O'Meara chose for his books dealt with exciting episodes from the frontier period of American history, some of which occurred in Northern Minnesota.

O'Meara was born in Cloquet, Minnesota, the son of a timber scaler who had spent some thirty winters in the logging camps during the 1880s, 90s and early 1900s. When asked how he came to write *The Trees Went Forth,* he said, "the answer is simple enough. I had always wanted to write, and it was natural that my first novel, like most first novels, should be auto-biographical . . . I based it on a personal experience I thought might be interesting to others."

When O'Meara was nineteen years old, he spent a winter in a northern Minnesota logging camp. O'Meara tells us, "the camp boss was Ed "Pine City" Netser, one of the last great boss loggers in the Cloquet area. with a crew of a hundred men, he built his camps, laid out his roads, cut over seven million feet of pine, landed it on Pequawan Lake, and drove it down the St. Louis River to the mills in Cloquet. And he did it in the classic 'horse logging' style without an ounce of steam."

O'Meara continues, "even then I was developing a sense of history, and I suspected that I was witnessing the last chapter of a great and colorful American epoch. I decided that some day I would write a book about Netser's camp. So I carefully observed everything about me, the camp layout and equipment, the crew and the kind of life they led, all the details of cutting, hauling, and landing timber. Years later, I checked my observations and impressions with my father . . . he was an accurate observer with a total recall memory, and I decided it would be a service to history, as well as to myself as a future writer, to record everything he knew about logging camps and logging . . . When I finally got around to writing *The Trees Went Forth* in 1947 — these notes, together with my own memories of Netser's camp, gave me a solid historical basis for what I thought of as a 'documentary novel.' While the story told in *The Trees Went Forth* is pure invention, and all the characters fictional, every detail of camp life and logging operations is, I believe, scrupulously correct."

A number of years ago, I had the pleasure of meeting Walter O'Meara and reading several of his historical novels, including *The Trees Went Forth.* I was impressed with the historical accuracy of his books. When the Forest History Center at Grand Rapids, Minnesota began its development and the decision to reconstruct a 1900 period Minnesota logging camp was made, we sought help and advice from Walter O'Meara. It was most fortunate that O'Meara donated his original notes and accurate sketches on logging camps and their furnishings to the Minnesota Historical Society for use in reconstructing the camp which now exists at the Center.

The Minnesota Historical Society, the Forest History Center, and the readers of this book will be deeply indebted to O'Meara for his important contribution to the history of a dramatic period in American History.

Robert C. Wheeler

October, 1982
Robert C. Wheeler is a retired Associate Director of the Minnesota Historical Society

To

My Father

*and to all the vanished race of shanty boys
and rivermen, and to their women who,
like my mother, kept lone care of their
homes and children through the long winters, this story of Patrick Dempsey's camp
on the Wolf is affectionately dedicated.*

*All of the characters in this book—
Patrick Dempsey, Jennie Keeler, Cherry
Gordon, Sari Luomala, and the others—
are imaginary. So also are the places
—Mokoman, the St. Pierre, and the rest;
so far as I am aware, none are to be
found on any map of Minnesota. The
story, too, is wholly fictitious.*

The Trees Went Forth

CHAPTER ONE

I

I WAS awakened that night by the jangling of our front door bell. I met my mother at the head of the stairs; she stood there silent and trembling in the darkness, an overcoat thrown over her nightgown.

"I'm afraid to go down, Matt," she whispered. "It's been ringing quite a long time. You—you see what it is, Matt."

"There, Ma," I said. "You go cover up. You'll catch cold standing there. It's probably nothing, Ma."

But I knew better. In Mokoman people did not ring your doorbell in the middle of the night unless something was mighty wrong. It wasn't my father down there, I knew. If my father had been taken sick at the sawmill, or if the mill had broken down, he would have come in through the back door; it was always unlocked.

I opened the front door. A man was standing on the porch with his back toward me. He turned around, and I saw that it was Dan Curry, an old friend of my father's.

Without saying anything, Dan stepped into the house and took off his hat. He held out his hand to me.

After a little while he said, "It's about your Pa, lad." He looked up the stairs, as though to make sure we were

11

alone, and his voice dropped to a whisper. "It's bad news I've got about him."

Dan pressed my hand a little harder, and I understood well enough what he was trying to tell me. But I had to make dead sure; I had to hear him say it.

"Is he hurt bad?" I asked. "Or—or—"

"Aye, he's bad hurt, lad," Dan said softly. He put his hat back on his head. "You've got to know it all—he's—dead. . . ."

"Where is he?"

Dan hesitated. "Well, you see . . . we thought maybe on account of how—well, we figured we better take him over and get him fixed up a little afore your Ma sees him."

"Will you wait a minute, Dan?" I asked. "I'll get dressed and go back with you."

I went slowly upstairs to tell my mother what she already knew.

II

Several days after we had buried my father in the stump-dotted cemetery west of town, I told my mother about my not returning to the University.

"Well, Ma," I said lightly, "I guess the old Alma Mater will have to get along without me this year."

She bent over her embroidery frame and made no answer, as if she had not heard me. Her deft red fingers pushed the needle in and out, methodically; her plain, serious face remained intent on her work.

"I've decided not to go back to school this fall, Ma."

I knew how hard a thing it was for her to hear. In the year 1906 not many boys from Mokoman were attending the University—especially not many from the families of sawmill workers. It was a sort of distinction we had, our family had: my going to the "U." And my mother was so very proud of it—prouder, perhaps, than she had ever been of anything in her life.

"Maybe we could figure some way to work it, Matt," she said finally.

She knew we couldn't. My father had left some insurance, but not enough to support us for very long—let alone send me to college. But she said it anyhow.

"There might be some way."

"Not this year, Ma," I said. "I've been thinking. It's maybe a good thing to take this year out, anyhow. Sort of give me a chance to think things over—what I want to do afterwards, and everything."

"I'm afraid if you drop out you'll never go back, Matt. That's all's worrying me."

"Oh, sure, Ma. Sure, I'll go back. Maybe *next* year."

My mother got up, out of her rocking chair, and laid her needlework on the table. She stood strangely still and, it seemed, undecided—as though her intention, whatever it might have been, had suddenly faded from her mind.

"Just you don't worry now," I said helplessly. "Carlie and me'll look after you. We'll get along fine—and I'll go back to school *next* year. You wait and see, Ma."

"I know, Matt." She did smile a little, as though remembering some pleasant thing. "That's what your Pa always says. . . . We'll get along fine. . . ."

Because he had said he might be able to help me, I went to see Dan Curry about getting a job in the woods for the winter. I found him in the tiny lobby of Ryan's boarding house, swapping stories with several cronies on the night shift. Dan was in the middle of one of those Pat-and-Mike tales which still constituted so large a part of American humor at the turn of the century.

"So Pat and Mike leans on their picks and they watches this steam-shovel for a while," he was saying, "and finally Pat says, 'Well, ye can puff, and ye can grunt, and ye can throw dirt around—but ye can't vote th' straight Dimmy-cratic ticket, ye son-of-a-bitch!' "

Dan got up amid the laughter and came over to me. He was a trim, squarely-built man, with a well-weathered face and crisp gray hair. He had once been an amateur fighter, and was supposed to have trained with Corbett. But he was a gentle-spoken man, with smiling, cloudy blue eyes.

"How are you, lad?" he inquired, holding out his hand. "And your Ma?"

"She's fine, thanks," I answered. "We're all fine, Dan. I came over to see you about that job—the one you thought Dempsey might have this winter."

I outlined briefly the situation in which my father's death had left our family, and the necessity of my obtaining work.

"I don't know where a feller'd find Pat Dempsey right now," Dan said. "But I'm pretty sure where he'll be after

14

supper. He'll be over to the Point, most likely. Come back 'bout seven o'clock, Matt, and we'll wheel over and see if we can find him."

"Do you think there's a chance, Dan?" I asked.

"I hear Pat's thinkin' about puttin' on a clerk this winter," he said. "If he does, they's thirty a month in it, lad."

He winked encouragingly. Dan knew exactly how heavily my question was laden with hope, anxiety, a little fear perhaps, now that I bore the whole responsibility for our support—my mother's, my brother Carlie's and my own.

CHAPTER TWO

I

*T*HE SALOON in which Dan and I sought Dempsey was located on "the Point." The Point was a log-bound spit of land on the far side of the St. Pierre river, and on it were segregated all of Mokoman's fifteen saloons. The local brothel, a huge frame building, was still farther removed from the town, hidden in the woods beyond the river. By this arrangement the citizens of Mokoman had succeeded in confining most of the community's fighting, brawling and hell-raising to an isolated and restricted area. The lumberjacks and rivermen, on the other hand, were allowed a place for free and unrestrained enjoyment of their leisure time. It was therefore an arrangement approved by all.

Dan and I crossed the red wooden bridge to the Point in the dusk of a late September evening. A single street ran parallel to the river. Along this street a row of saloons turned their dirty, smeary faces toward the town—box-like frame buildings, each with its proprietor's name in large, unashamed letters across its dicky front: Thomas McGough, Davy Ryan, Peter Curry, T. J. Proctor. The street was illuminated only by a sputtering arc light at the bridge, and by the greasy glow of the saloon windows.

16

It was noisy that night with talk and shouts, and sometimes bursts of laughter. A pair of swinging doors flew open and two scuffling men rolled out upon the wooden sidewalk. A large man in a white apron followed them, kicked at them vigorously a few times, and went back into the saloon. The men scrambled to their feet, shouted blood-chilling imprecations through the door, then lurched arm-in-arm down the street.

I had never been on the Point at night before, although I had often crossed to it as a boy on my way to the woods beyond the river. Once I had seen a bartender carry a man from a saloon and hold him for a while, kicking and yelling, over the rail that ran along the water. Once I had seen a woman following a drunken man in the street and shouting foul words at him in a strident voice. And once we had seen a dead man, with flies crawling on his hands, lying on the sidewalk, and a little group of quiet men standing near, waiting for the coroner to come. The Point was a place where strange, unaccountable and improper things happened, and small boys were cautioned by their parents to keep away from it. I had never been in any of the saloons.

"We'll likely find him in Joe McKinnon's place," Dan said.

I followed him through the doors. The saloon was filled with rivermen and sawmill workers. Most of the men were dressed in their work clothes, the rivermen distinguishable by their stagged pants and caulked boots, the mill hands by the white dust on their hats and shoes. The air in the place was heated and foul. We found Dempsey at the center of the bar.

There are few still alive, I suppose, who can recall the famous bosses of the northern Minnesota camps at the century's turning. Yet they were men of great renown in their day, strong, colorful men, given often to heroic vices as well as uncommon virtues, and sometimes to Gargantuan folly: Mike Sullivan, Tom Mogan, Charlie Kellar, Ed Netser, Mushhead Higgins, Nick Sloan, Peter Dempsey, Tom Lynch, Terry Lynch, Jack Chisholm, Dinny Doyle, Andy Gowan, George Dixon, Duncan Campbell, Jim Healy, John G. Long . . . great men all, and no logger in the Minnesota woods but had a certain pride in working for any one of them. But "I'm going up for Dempsey" was spoken with a special nonchalance.

The caulks in Dempsey's driving boots sank deep into the pine plank flooring of McKinnon's saloon. He was a big man, and he could throw a pike-pole farther than any logger on the St. Pierre. He had tousled blond hair, rather small and pale gray eyes; his skin was rawhide; he was tough and leathery-looking. When he smiled, he inclined his head and slanted his gaze up at you from under his bushy blond eyebrows. A little trickle of tobacco juice wandered down through the bristles on his chin.

At one time Dempsey had been a great drinker and a troublesome one. Loggers told of the Sunday morning he had been found with his hair frozen into the ice of Mokoman's principal street—so firmly imbedded that it had been necessary to chop him out with an ax! They recalled the memorable occasion of his climbing up on the bar in O'Sullivan's saloon and walking its length, kicking off the glasses of the astonished customers. Many of the stories must have been apocryphal, yet the general legend most certainly had a background of truth—for the tales persisted long after Dempsey had ceased to be a drinking man, even long after he had died.

There was no doubt that Patrick Dempsey had been a wild and bothersome character before he settled down. And it was quite a wonder to those who remembered his younger days that he should have turned out to be the steady, efficient camp foreman that everyone in Mokoman knew him to be.

Somewhat in awe, I stood before this mighty man.

"Pat, I'd like for you to know Matt, here," Dan Curry said. "Jim Bradley's boy."

Dempsey scrutinized me critically from under his bushy brows.

"Jim Bradley's boy," he repeated slowly. "Guess I damn well *ought* t' know him," he said. "Didn't I spell his old man when he come down from Hank Sloan's camp, time th' lad himself here was born?"

He regarded me with an air of proprietorship.

"Winter of '87," he said confidently. "And a damn cold one, too."

He beamed at me as though he were in some measure responsible for my being there nineteen years later.

"Well, yer a dead ringer fer yer dad," he said finally.

"If ye turn out half th' man he was, ye'll be all right!"

Dan laughed appreciatively. "Don't worry about him, Pat," he said.

He and Dempsey fell into conversation. Their talk was mostly about the coming winter's operations. Some forty camps were in prospect, it seemed, a few of which were already building. There was a scarcity of men, however, and the return of workers from the Dakota harvest fields was awaited with some impatience. . . . John Hurley expected to cut seven million feet or more for the Zenith Lumber Company on the Ojibway. . . . Dangling Dailey had prophesied an open winter. . . .

"I hear you're takin' up a clerk this year," Dan remarked.

"I'm thinkin' about it," Dempsey said impressively.

Like half the camp bosses of his time, Dempsey could read but little and could write only his own name. With the help of some literate member of his crew—a scaler generally—he had hitherto made shift to order his own supplies for cook-camp, wannigan and stock, make out his own time, and keep his own records. But the lumber companies were growing more exacting, and the "clerk" was beginning to make his appearance, here and there, in the larger camps.

"Matt, here, would like to go up for you."

Dempsey looked me over again, then poured himself another drink.

"Can ye cypher?" he asked suddenly. He leaned back against the bar, enfolding his empty shot glass in a huge fist and looking at me, the way Dempsey did, as if he were peering over a pair of invisible spectacles.

"Yes, sir," I gulped.

"How many pounds in a bale of hay?"

The question caught me flat-footed and defenseless. I opened my mouth, but no answer came out. I had none. In the cruel publicness of McKinnon's saloon I stood confused and miserable in my stark ignorance.

"In a bale of hay," Dempsey repeated slowly, "how many pounds?"

Some of the men at the bar, mill hands and rivermen, snickered as I tried frantically to recall the table of weights and measures in the back of the arithmetic. I saw their sly grins through a haze of embarrassment.

"D'ye mean they never learned ye that in college?"

"No, sir."

"Well, I'll tell ye something, then, those fellers in college never told ye. Now pay 'tenshun." He paused for emphasis. "In a bale of hay . . . they is . . . approximately . . . one hunerd pounds. Got that?"

"Yes, sir."

"Well, don't fergit it. And don't fergit who told ye. Old Pat Dempsey told ye."

Pleased with himself, he poured another drink from the bottle on the bar, and when he spoke again it was to Dan.

"Hell, it ain't his fault if them professors never told him," he said grandly. "I ain't holdin' that against him none. I like the looks of th' lad, Dan. Looks like his old man."

He held out his hand, lowered his head and smiled. "Okay, lad," he said. "Ye're goin' up fer Dempsey."

II

After it had been thus agreed that I was to work for Dempsey, we all had a drink to "wet down" the bargain.

I was not used to whiskey, and, much to Dempsey's amusement, I choked a little on mine. As I turned away from the bar to hide my confusion, I inadvertently jostled the man standing next to me.

"Ya spilled my drink," the man said.

He thrust his face close to mine. It was an angry face, and, with the whiskey dripping from its chin, a somewhat ludicrous one. The other men at the bar guffawed.

"Ya spilled my drink," the man repeated insistently.

"I'm sorry," I said. "I'm—"

"Sorry ain't enough, kid."

Dan slapped the man on the shoulder placatingly and tossed a half-dollar on the bar.

"Forget it, Joe," he said. "The lad's sorry—didn't he say he is? Have one on me."

The man studied me in resentful silence for perhaps five seconds, then turned and tipped the bottle. He scowled at me over his drink.

"Well, no hard feelin's," he said. "I'll be seein' ya." He downed his liquor. "I hope t' tell ya!" he added, with an unpleasant smile.

Dan and I left the saloon. I said good-by to him and hurried home to tell my good news to my mother.

She was in the kitchen, at the ironing board, when I came in.

"I got it, Ma!" I cried, all of my elation bursting forth at once. "I'm going up for Dempsey!"

I could not understand why my mother did not say anything—did not even look up, but continued silently and carefully to smooth with the hot iron the already smooth cuff of my white Sunday shirt.

CHAPTER THREE

I

I WAS DOING only what many another boy my age had done in Mokoman—what nearly all of Mokoman's men did each autumn. During the summer they worked in the sawmills and lumber yards. But in the winter, when the great cold set in, they went to the camps, and Mokoman became a town populated by women and children through the long, drear months of the logging season. For the great pine forests were the source of everything in Mokoman. Lumber was Mokoman's life.

Into this town had come the westward-surging flood of loggers from the great lumbering centers of Michigan and Wisconsin—the shanty boys and the river hogs of Bay City and Saginaw, of Muskegon and Eau Claire and Chippewa Falls. Here, unknowingly, they came for their last fling and their last stand; for Mokoman was, in fact, the last great sawmill town east of the prairies. After Mokoman, lumbering in the old, grand style ceased forever. But nobody, of course, could know that in 1906.

In that year the town had five great sawmills going day and night in ten-hour shifts. Into their dripping maws disappeared millions of white pine logs, and from them were disgorged billions of feet of sweet-smelling boards and timbers. Wood was everywhere in Mokoman. From bank to bank the river was filled with saw logs floated down the deep St. Pierre, a hundred miles or more, to feed the hungry mills. Lumber was piled high in beautiful, symmetrical stacks along the river's edge: row on row, with plank-paved streets and grassy alleys in between, a sort of wooden city in itself. All the sidewalks in Mokoman were of wood; much of the ground beneath your feet was sawdust. And every building in Mokoman—the homes, the stores, the churches and the school—of course, was built of wood.

Upon this wooden city, by mid-October, the long Minnesota winter had begun to tighten its relentless grip, and life slowed down to a drab and dragging thing. The river froze solid in late November, and, with the close of the sawing season, mill workers and rivermen laid aside their overalls and caulked boots and put on the mackinaw of the logger. They left for the distant camps quite suddenly, sometimes as many as a thousand in a single week, trickling northward along the tote-roads and frozen river courses like a straggling army in retreat. Each year Mokoman emptied itself thus of most of its men, keeping back only the women and children, and those too old to stand the rigors of the camps. Then the great snows came down, the temperature dropped far below zero, sometimes for weeks at a time; and the town wrapped itself in a frigid somnolence until, late in March, winter broke at last, and the men returned, whiskery and unshorn, and with the redolence of the pine woods clinging to them.

25

And I, in the fall of the year 1906, was one of those who left Mokoman for the distant northern camps.

II

The night before I went, my mother had laid out neatly, on the dining room table, the clothing and a few personal belongings I would take with me to camp in the morning. I checked off each item methodically; it was a way of taking my mind off the thing I had to do presently.

I placed everything in a little pile: the two suits of underwear that had been my father's—thick and heavy and pure wool, to keep out the cold that sometimes dropped to nearly fifty degrees below zero in January; six pairs of gray wool "German" sox, a little stock of blue and red bandana handkerchiefs, a "stag" shirt. I opened the cigar box that held my razor, shaving soap and brush, my comb and toothbrush, a bottle of Pine Tar cough syrup, and a little pack of needles, thread and mending yarn. I noted that my mother had included my rosary and prayer book.

That was about all I would need to take with me for a winter in the woods. Everything else I wore, or carried in my pockets, or could obtain later from the camp wannigan. I had already changed to my woods clothing—warm woolen underwear and socks next to my skin, gray MacMillan trousers hacked off with a jack-knife midway between knee and ankle, rubber footgear with ten-inch leather tops and sheepskin inner soles, a "Scotch" cap topped by a pompon, striped wool mittens inside horsehide leather ones, a flannel shirt over which, before I left, I would button my mackinaw.

This was very nearly the standard rig of the Minnesota lumberjack in the early nineteen hundreds. Sometimes a small black Stetson hat replaced the cap. Now and then shoepacks and even ankle-high moccasins appeared in the camps; sheepskin jackets were occasionally worn; and there were always those who, through poverty or unfamiliarity with the customs of the woods, presented themselves in strange and unorthodox gear. Chief among the latter were the Indians and men new to the country, such as the Swedes, Norwegians and a few stray Finns.

Generations of loggers, however—whacking their way through white pine and Norway timber, in cold and wet, all the way from Quebec to the western prairies—had worked out this simple outfit as the warmest and driest, the one that gave freest play to the muscles and best protected one against chill and rheumatism. And it had become as uniform in the woods of northern Minnesota as were the Levi's and the Stetson on the Montana plains.

I stowed my things away carefully in my turkey, a laundered flour sack which, when fully packed, could be slung over the shoulder by a short length of rope. I closed the sack, and knotted the free end of the rope around it. I hefted the turkey, dropped it on a chair, and reached for my mackinaw.

"Gosh, I wish't I was going with you," Carlie said enviously.

I faced my younger brother sternly.

"Listen, kiddo," I said, "you just remember what I told

you this morning. While I'm away, you're watching out for Ma and this house. You're going to keep the woodbox and reservoir *filled,* and the snow shovelled and the ashes emptied, and without being told all the time. When it snows, you're going to bank the house good. And you're going—"

"Yeah, I know, I know," Carlie said. "I'll watch out for Ma all right." He sidled over to her and put his arm around her waist, grinning.

"Sure he will, Matt," my mother said. "Don't worry about us. Me and Carlie'll get along all right."

"Well, Ma, I guess I might as well get going."

It had been decided that, since the start for Dempsey's camp would be made at daylight, I was to stay the night with Dan Curry at Ryan's boarding house; and Dan would arrange a ride for me on one of the tote-wagons going up in the morning.

"Well, Ma," I said, "I'm off then."

I held out my arms, and my mother came and gave me a hug and a kiss.

"Good-by, Matt," she said, "and be careful for yourself." Suddenly she began to cry.

"There, there, Ma," I said. "Maybe I'll get down for Christmas. I'll see if I can't work it."

"Try to, Matt." She smiled with her wet eyes. "And," half serious, half bantering, "don't forget to say your prayers."

"I won't, Ma." I made a sudden lunge at Carlie, caught him and rumpled his hair. " 'By, Carlie—take good care of everything."

"Sure I will, Matt—what d' you think?"

I waved to the two figures standing in the lamp-lit doorway. I waved to them, and they both waved back.

For almost twenty winters my mother had said good-by to my father in just such a way. In Mokoman, every year, nearly all the women sent away their men folk in the same manner, and did not see them again until the camps broke and the crews swarmed down in the spring. . . . My mother had hoped that it would be different with her and me.

III

It was still night outside as Dan and I left Ryan's boarding house for the Point—a sharp, clear night, cold and glittering, with gleaming hoar-frost over everything, and the sky full of glinting stars.

The great North Mill was ablaze with light, and the saws shrilled as they tore hungrily through the logs; ripping off their oozing slabs and boards; hurrying, hurrying before ice filled the mill pond and put an end to the sawing season. The saws shrieked, the carriages rumbled as they swept past the diamond-shaped windows of the mill. And, back of these nearer, more boldly defined sounds, the night was filled with the distant hum and murmur of the other mills. The night was laden, too, with odors. The rich, heavy smell of new-cut timber, steaming wet and warm from the friction of the saws. The thinner, sharper fragrance of lumber drying in the yards. The smell of the river. And the smeech of fires that, at this time of year, were always smoldering in the bush.

The arc lights were burning on the Point as we crossed the bridge, and the dirty windows of the saloons stared out across the river like a row of hollow, sunken eyes. A gray cat wandered out from between two buildings, skittered suddenly under the board sidewalk.

We arrived at the loading dock of the Zenith Lumber Company, where the big, high-wheeled tote-wagons were waiting to begin their long treks to the northern camps. They had been loaded during the night, a ton to each wagon, with supplies and equipment, food for the crews, and building materials. The teamsters were already arriving, plodding along behind their heavy four-horse teams, the reins trailing for yards behind them on the frosty ground. Benson was one of the first to show up. He was a rather small man, humped over the way teamsters are.

"How 'ya this morning, Ed?" Dan asked, by way of greeting.

Benson, without answering, pushed and pulled at his big horses, cursing doggedly as he maneuvered them into position for hitching to the wagon. His task completed, he looked resentfully, it seemed, at Dan.

"Look at them goddam horses," he said. "Did yuh ever see such a goddam, no-good team of goddam broken down—"

His simple vocabulary having, apparently, failed him at this point, he glared balefully at the animals.

To me they appeared perfectly sound and strong; but Dan nodded sympathetically.

"Yeah, they look purty bad," he agreed. "Ed, I'd like for you—"

"Th' goddam company can't afford no better," resumed Benson sarcastically. "They're too goddam pore."

He scooped a chew of snuff from his lip with his forefinger, and shook it to the ground.

"The son-of-a-bitches."

"Ed," said Dan again, "this is the lad that's goin' up with you this mornin'. Goin' to clerk for Dempsey."

Benson paused in the act of taking the cover off his snuff box. He shrugged his shoulders and started for the little "office" at the far end of the loading dock.

"Well, throw up your turkey," he called back, "and climb on. Soon's I get my ticket we'll be wheelin'."

Dan held out his hand to me. "So long, lad," he said. "And take it easy."

"Good-by, Dan." I shook his hand. "Hope I'll be seeing you."

I climbed up on the driver's seat and stowed my turkey in a crevice in the load. Benson reappeared, stuffing a folded sheet of yellow paper into the pocket of his shirt. He sprang up beside me with surprising agility, took his long whip from the socket, and cracked it over the lead horses.

"Whup! Whup! Git up, ye goddam son-of-a-bitches!" he shouted, and the big animals threw themselves against the traces.

The shape of things, shadowy and cold, without color, had just begun to form in the misty pre-dawn light as we rumbled over the track that led from the Point to the east bank of the river . . . and to the Old Road.

CHAPTER FOUR

I

FOR MORE than fifty miles the Old Road squirmed and twisted its way north and west. It was the main stem in a vast system of tote-roads which, with its roots in Mokoman, spread like a tree of life on a Numbah rug through a thousand square miles of Minnesota wilderness.

There were other tote-roads too: those, for example, that followed the St. Louis and Floodwood rivers; the Miller Trunk, which flowed southward from the Missabe Range, like a river and its tributaries, into Duluth; and the Swan Lake road, which pushed westward from the head of the lakes to the great "ox-bow" of the St. Louis.

In winter, the rivers themselves were used for hauling, and on the St. Pierre alone the great tote-sleighs, each loaded with its two tons of camp supplies, would form almost continuous processions coming and going to the woods. The big open bells made cheerful music up and down the river as the two-horse sleigh teams pounded out their twenty-five to thirty miles a day on the ice.

But until the broad St. Pierre and its tributaries were frozen solid early in December, many of the forty-odd camps that based their operations on Mokoman still depended for equipment and supplies upon the tote-roads that had been hacked through hundreds of miles of brush and swamp and timber. And of these, the Old Road was one of the most important.

The Old Road followed, like an afternoon shadow, the east bank of the St. Pierre. Its terminus was about fifty miles northwest of Mokoman; but so tortuous was its course that the wagons traveled almost twice that distance over its full length. Like the branches of a great tree, secondary roads took off from the Old Road at intervals, usually to follow some tributary of the river; and, like twigs, still lesser roads took off from these. And so the way was opened through the whole St. Pierre River system for the big tote-teams.

Benson and I were taking the Old Road as far as the confluence of the St. Pierre and Ojibway Rivers, about thirty miles north. Then we were to turn north and east along the west bank of the Ojibway for another ten or twelve miles; then due east for a few miles to the site of Dempsey's new camps on the Wolf. It was, at that time of year, a hard two-day trip.

Our tote-wagon was almost, but not quite, typical of the heavy Deering wagons that were commonly used for hauling. It had the usual over-sized wheels, with long spokes and heavy rims, necessary to cope with the pot holes, tree roots and boulders on the roads. But it had been built in the Zenith Lumber Company's own shops, stouter and heavier than was usual, with huge axles and hubs so large that they resembled beer kegs. With a full ton of weight aboard, even Benson's fresh, strong horses —each weighing at least 1,600 pounds—were forced to struggle with the load as we pulled up the Big Hill immediately across the river.

At the top of the Big Hill Benson gave his horses a breather, and I took the last look that I should have, for many a long month, at Mokoman. A white plume of wood smoke rose into the air from every chimney of every small frame house. The mills were quiet, between shifts, and the streets were dotted with moving ant-like specks —the night crews returning home, and the day shifts going to work in the gray half-light of early dawn.

This was the second time that I had ever gone away from this little town. The first was when I went to the University. I had been a little afraid then, and had even trembled as the train pulled out—whether because of the separation from the only people and the only places I had ever known, or because of excitement and the anticipation of strange new things to be experienced. . . . But this time it was all different. This journey could have but one sad meaning—the breaking off of all my plans, the abandoning of all my hopes; and I felt very low in spirit as I looked back at Mokoman through the morning mists.

II

"Whayahgodagup!"

Benson, with a crack of his long whip, shattered the still air with a loud and wholly unintelligible command. His horses stolidly and leisurely tensed the muscles of their great legs, leaned forward with heads down; and the wagon started on its way again.

It left behind it four ribbon-like tracks in the hoar-frost that covered the road. We passed through the Indian Village on the Big Hill, and by the church that black-bearded Father Gautier had built with his own hands. The sun came up and the countryside was all aglitter with the frost, each tree and blade of grass and withered stock of fireweed. The roofs of some low log buildings—the homes of Indians on the reservation—sparkled white and pink in the thin, cold light. There were only a few such buildings, and they became rarer as we jolted, high above the log-jammed waters of the St. Pierre, over the twisting gradients of the Old Road.

For the most part, our route wound through vast stretches of slashings—the desolate debris of past logging operations—in which the second growth of birch and poplar had already taken hold. In some places fire had run through the cutover, charring the tangled mass of woods wreckage, and blackening the very boulders which the glaciers had strewn everywhere. There was little timber left in these parts, save for a patch now and then, following with geometric precision the town and section lines.

As the sun rose higher the frost melted, lying longest in the shadows of standing trees and on the western side of fallen logs and branches. It was the time of day when the woods are astir with their own people. At almost every turn, coveys of partridge, scratching in the gravel of the road, whirred off in curving flight. Jack rabbits looped in long jumps through the slashings. And once I caught sight of half a dozen brush deer, their white "flags" bobbing up and down as they melted into the frost-wet undergrowth.

While observing these things, I clung to the driver's seat, a section of planking affixed to a pair of long spring-poles of birch, and upholstered with a hay-stuffed feed sack. Now and again, as we careened over a boulder or a tree root, or dropped into a pot hole, this seat whipped sharply up and down, and I was forced to hold tightly to it, or else be catapulted off. Benson, on the other hand, seemed to possess some quality of adhesiveness which kept him securely and apparently without effort attached to his seat. He sat beside me in sour contemplation of his horses' heaving rears, spitting at astonishingly regular intervals, and saying absolutely nothing. It was almost mid-morning when, as we passed an old, abandoned set of camps, he finally spoke to me.

"Them is Dorsey's old camps," he volunteered. "It was th' lousiest goddam layout a man ever worked in. I toted fer it in '96."

Benson gave the ancient establishment no further notice.

"Back in them days," he added acidly, "young punks didn't get no rides to where they was goin'." He spat. "They goddam well put their turkeys on their backs and hoofed." He spat again. "They *hoofed,* goddam it."

I thought it best not to reply to this, and the old man, in turn, lapsed once more into gloomy silence. When we passed other tote-wagons, however, returning empty to Mokoman, Benson cheerfully and profanely gave back the other drivers' greetings as they maneuvered their wagons past each other on the narrow road. Perhaps, I decided, Benson simply didn't like me.

Shortly after noon we stopped at a homesteader's and obtained coffee to drink with our lunch of beef sandwiches and blueberry pie. Benson gave each of the horses a measure of oats, without water, and allowed the animals an hour's rest. The "nooning" over, he cracked his whip, cursed his team with professional zeal, and we rolled northward once more.

The sun was setting when, shortly after five o'clock, we arrived at the juncture of the St. Pierre and Ojibway Rivers. There was a bridge across the St. Pierre here. In a clearing a two-story frame house, kept company by a barn and several outbuildings, stood dejectedly in the gathering dusk. This was Mrs. Duffy's place, where tote-teamsters on their way to the up-river camps spent their first night out from Mokoman.

I helped Benson unharness the horses, then trudged down to the river to fetch them water. On the opposite side of the stream a tote-wagon, its rear wheels chained to prevent their turning, slithered down the steep grade of the Moose Lake Road, the horses back on their haunches, the driver shouting frantically. Tired and hungry, I stood watching until the teamster had brought his outfit safely to the bridge-head. I filled my buckets and started up the bank; the cold water slopped over my knees and down my legs. I watered the horses, washed, and went in to supper —too weary to be hungry.

After supper, the men who were putting up for the night at Mrs. Duffy's—a half-dozen teamsters and a couple of timber cruisers—sat on kitchen chairs around the stove in the "sitting room." Most of them lit short-stemmed briar pipes, of the variety called "nose warmers" in the woods, and presently the air was murky with the smoke of Peerless and Standard. The men exchanged news and gossip of the camps in a curious, telegraphic kind of speech that was often almost as unintelligible as a foreign language.

There was a tall, gaunt man with a pinkish growth of beard on his lantern jaws, and with only the stumps of a few teeth in his mouth. I recognized him as the Whiteface Liar, a character widely known in all the camps, and noted as a story teller. He was relating some experience to a tote-teamster from Bannon's camp; but he was aware of the attention which the rest of the group was giving his yarn.

The Whiteface Liar carefully shaved off a ration of chewing tobacco from his plug of Spearhead, and slowly placed it in his mouth.

"Yes, sir," he said, "this here boiler fin'lly quits, on account of the lads grumblin' so and talkin' some about tossin' him in a blanket. So he wheels fer town and there we was left—left without no cook and in a most distressin' situation.

"Well, Mushhead Higgins (he was th' push) says, 'Lads, they is just one thing fer us t' do. Somebody has got t' cook fer this crew ontil we can get a proper cook up from town. I do be callin' for volunteers.'

"But they wa'n't no volunteers, which was onderstandable, after th' whole crew seein' Beefslew Jackson heave th' coffee pot at th' boiler's head only th' day before.

" 'Very well, me lads,' says Mushhead, 'we will now draw lots fer th' honor of officiatin' in th' cook shanty.'

"Some of th' lads objected on th' grounds of onnatural jepardy, but they was over-ruled by th' more sober minded and hongry. So we draws lots out of Mushhead's hat.

"Th' onlucky lad was a feller named Sam McTigue. He looks kinda glum, as a feller would expect, but he's game enough.

" 'All right,' Mac says, 'all right, me bully boys, I do be dishin' up yer beans fer ye. But on one condition,' he says, 'I'm standin' fer no disparagin' remarks,' he says.

" 'They'll be none of th' same,' says Mushhead Higgins.

" 'And th' first that makes any complaint whatsoever about my cookin'—he gits me job,' says Mac. 'And is that fair?'

"Well, everybody agrees that's fair and reasonable enough. So McTigue sets t' work gettin' breakfast th' next mornin'.' "

The Whiteface Liar's face was momentarily clouded with an expression of anguish.

"They was no doubt that Mac was willin'," he resumed after a pause that somewhat resembled a shudder. "But th' results of his cookin' was somethin' fierce. . . .

"They was somethin' fierce," he repeated solemnly. "Most of th' men was tooken with a sudden loss of appetite. But nobody said nothin', of course, on account of that agreement that the first feller complained had t' take over th' job hisself.

"There was one big swamper, though, big Swede name of Pedersen, that was specially distressful. They was tears in both his eyes when he tasted them flapjacks.

" 'Holy Old Yumpin' Yesus!' says this swamper, 'vill yu look at them flapjacks—burned on both sides an' raw in th' middle!'

"Then he looks up and who does he see but McTigue, smilin' at him sweet and encouragin'-like.

" *'Yoost th' way aye like 'em!'* yells the swamper."

The Liar's story drew a few appreciative guffaws from the men, and a high cackle from Mrs. Duffy, a plump little woman who had appeared in the doorway, winding an alarm clock.

"Seems to me, Whiteface," a teamster remarked dryly, "seems to me th' last time I heard ye tell that one, it was beans instead o' flapjacks."

"Ye're mistaken, Tooney," said the Liar with dignity. "You do be mindin' th' double-barrelled bean hole at Paddy Dolan's camp on th' Little Moosehorn. Now there was a most onusual . . ."

The Liar, however, was not encouraged to continue. As if by pre-arranged signal, the men arose, knocked the ashes from their pipes into the sand-box on the floor, and filed outside to relieve themselves before retiring.

I shared a bed that night with a horse doctor who had come in late on his way to Camp Lynch. He was a huge, be-whiskered man who snored titanically throughout the night, and waged a relentless campaign for most of the bed and all of the blankets.

IV

By daylight we were again rattling along a corduroy road that followed the Ojibway River. This stream, one of the main tributaries of the St. Pierre, was cluttered with booms and other paraphernalia of logging. Millions of feet of saw logs had been driven down the Ojibway to the mills at Mokoman. And close-by was the scene of the famous jam at Lawrence's Eddy.

Several miles upstream we passed the narrows where it had occurred. Often I had heard my father tell of it: how Jack Allen had sworn that he could drive every log in the 'Jib in forty days, or eat what was left over; how the logs had got ahead of the water and piled up twenty feet high in the narrows; and how it had taken a month, at a cost of more than $40,000 in wages and dynamite, to break the jam—all, of course, to the immense and everlasting discomfiture of Mr. Allen.

The road continued to hold its meandering course northeast. The terrain grew rougher. Jagged out-croppings of the Canadian Shield—the oldest rock in all the world—alternated with small lakes and stretches of muskeg, and swamps where the autumn tamaracks burned like golden fires against the somber spruce. It was a country scarred by glaciers, blackened by fire, desolated by the cutting tools of men. And the earth, as though to cover the shame of her mutilation, had thrown a veil of

41

silvery birch and poplar saplings over the scene. No pine, neither the dark white pine nor the clean red Norway, would ever grow here again.

Toward noon we came to an odd-looking settlement of several log houses. One of the buildings was quite large and was constructed partly of sawn lumber. The curtains in the upstairs windows of this house parted as we arrived, and I could see the eyes of several women peering at us through the frosty panes. The women giggled and jostled each other. One put up her hand to adjust the window-shade, and the wide sleeve of her wrapper fell back to her shoulder. I could hear their laughter faintly through the glass.

This was Prouty's Corner. There was no crossroad here and no corner, but the place was called Prouty's Corner, nevertheless. It was located on the northern boundary of the government Indian reservation, and below it the sale of liquor was prohibited. This was the logger's last chance, on his way to the upper camps, to get a drink and avail himself of other accommodations discreetly provided by Prouty. Coming down, it was his first opportunity to dip into the fleshpots.

Prouty's Corner was seldom the scene of the lurid tales retold by lumberjacks and rivermen in barrooms, in bunkhouses, and around the camp fires of the drives. Vince Prouty, a huge man of dour countenance, conducted it along thoroughly practical and prosaic lines. There was no music in his barroom, no dance floor. There was little jollity at Prouty's; no one had ever been killed there.

We had a hot dinner served by a large blond slattern

who shuffled about in a pair of rubber boots such as the loggers wore. Benson had a drink of whiskey before the meal, and another afterwards. The liquor seemed to loosen his tongue.

"See them rapids?" he asked when, on the road again, we passed a turbulent stretch of river. "That there's where young Neely got drownded couple years ago." Benson cackled softly. "I seen it. Goddam, it was comical . . . comicalest sight I ever seen—that pore bastard flyin' through th' air like he did . . . him one way and his peavey th' other . . . an' Old Man Hall standin' there on th' bank pullin' his goddam nose . . ."

He cackled some more.

"Th' logs was piled ten, twenty feet high an' tighter 'n a bull's rear. An' there was young Neely, fer Christ's sake, hoppin' aroun' on them logs with a peavey, an' he's got a white shirt on, fer Christ's sake . . . An' all t' once he shoots up in th' air like a pigstickin' skyrocket an' when he come down it's jest too goddam bad, an' all the hollerin' an' nose-pullin' Old Man Hall done couldn't help young Neely none. . . . They didn't find him 'til th' next day, when they fished him out down t' th' Big Dam."

Benson helped himself to a load of snuff.

"Guess it was th' white shirt made it so goddam comical," he said.

We had crossed the Ojibway now, and were on a secondary road which followed a twisting north-westerly course inland. We would continue on this route until we had made Tobin's old camp—our temporary base while Dempsey's camp was being built.

43

The going was much more difficult than it had been earlier in the day; the road was now little more than a track through the cutover. It followed wherever possible, and however circuitous, the contours of the land, going around all obstacles, even large stumps and boulders. Hence, its course was almost never straight, seldom level; and at times the wagon tilted hazardously on the slopes and slanting shelves of rock. With increasing frequency, deep pot holes forced a pause in our journey until brush and poles could be cut and the holes filled up.

This task fell to me. Time and again, until the muscles of my thighs and shoulders ached, I climbed down from my seat, unstrapped the ax, and slashed away at the roadside alders until I had enough to level off the road. During these operations, Benson, perched like an ugly bird of evil on his high seat, made occasional obscene and uncomplimentary remarks. Once, as he observed my weary and none too expert handling of the ax, he let fly with a characteristic split expletive.

"Fer Christ's sake," he said, "Paddy Dempsey ain't none too per-goddam-ticular 'bout who goes up fer him no more!"

V

Darkness had occupied the muskegs and was creeping across the slashings when, at last, we arrived at Camp Tobin.

Benson tossed the reins down and sprang to the ground with a great show of agility. I climbed down after him, but slowly and painfully. I ached; I was chilled, too, and hungry, and beaten in spirit as Benson directed me to unhitch the horses.

"Kinda bushed, ain't ye?" he observed slyly. "You young punks ain't worth a hoot 'n hell no more—ye ain't worth a good goddam."

All at once I had had about as much of Benson as I could take.

"Listen here," I said, my fists clenched in my big mittens, and my voice, I guess, a little shaky, "I'm not *looking* for trouble, Benson, but if—if you—"

The grizzled old teamster paused in the act of dipping into his snuff box, and held a huge pinch poised in his thumb and first finger. He looked at me with startled little eyes; then he loosed one of his cackling laughs.

"Well, fer Christ-a-mighty!" he chortled, "Ye *must* be bushed. . . . Keep yer shirt on, son. G'wan in and git yerself a cupa coffee."

He tucked the snuff into his lower lip, took the lantern down from the driver's seat, and trailed off behind the horses, presumably toward the barn. Somewhat shamefacedly I picked up my turkey, which I had pitched from the wagon, and hoisted it to my shoulder. I looked about me miserably at Tobin's camp.

Half a dozen low log structures—bunkhouses, cookshanty, horse barn, and several other buildings of smaller size—lay in shadow at the edge of an unkempt clearing. High grass and some brush had grown up between the buildings. The place had a neglected, abandoned and, to me, infinitely depressing appearance.

At one time Tobin's camp had been headquarters camp for numerous operations along the Ojibway. In 1904 it became famous for a cut of ten million feet of white and Norway pine. But now it was maintained only as a sort of base for the Zenith Lumber Company's more remote establishments. It had become almost a ghost camp, with the gaunt and haunted look of all logging camps from which the crews, the horses and the subdued bustle of camp life have departed. Almost, but not quite—for a blue strand of smoke wavered upwards from the nearest building, and a light glowed in the end windows. Toward these, the only signs of human habitation in sight, I trudged dispiritedly.

The door of the camp opened just as I arrived in front of it, and a voice from somewhere inside—a woman's voice, loud and strong, yet warm and pleasant—called out:

"Somebody's just wheeled in, Cherry. Maybe it's Ted."

The girl who stood in the doorway against the light made no answer.

CHAPTER FIVE

I

*I*s it him?" the voice asked again.

"Naw, it's just somebody Benson brought in," the girl called back crossly.

She stood in the doorway like a black silhouette pasted against the rectangle of lamp light. Instead of a skirt, she wore denims—but there was no mistaking her sex. As I came up to the door, she stood aside to let me in. Her dark eyes—not the soft, warm kind—looked me over, and she made a hostile grimace with her small, sulky mouth.

"I suppose you did come in with Benson," she said noncommittally.

"Yes, he's out there," I said, "putting up the horses." I lowered my turkey to the floor. "My name's Bradley," I said. "Matthew Bradley."

"I know." She regarded me with a sort of bored curiosity. "Well, sit yourself at the table and Ma'll give you something to eat. I suppose you're hungry."

She waved toward an oilcloth-covered table, one of several in the big, dimly lit room, set with tin dishes for supper. Then she sauntered away. She wore moccasins, and the absence of heels gave her gait an exaggerated swaying motion.

"That," I thought, "would be Cherry Gordon." I had heard of her in Mokoman.

The woman with the loud, strong voice came forward from behind the cooking range. She was a big woman, pleasant and comfortable-looking, and a delicious fragrance of coffee and freshly baked bread seemed to accompany her. She held out her hand and beamed at me through steamy, gold-rimmed spectacles.

"So you're Jim Bradley's boy!" she exclaimed. "Well, *what* do you know!"

She kept my hand in her grasp, like a man. This was Jennie Keeler, I knew. I had heard about her also in Mokoman. She was a fine woman, everybody said, and a better man around camp than most. Summer and winter, she had been in the woods for a good many years now with her husband, Big Bill Keeler, camp watcher at Tobin.

Big Bill was a haunted man. Once, years before, he had killed a friend in a drunken brawl; and that was why he and Jennie now spent their days in the camps. It was the way she kept him sober—and not so much afraid. I met Big Bill later, of course, and found him to be a soft-spoken, friendly sort of man, with the gentle, detached manner that reformed drunkards often have.

As for Jennie, she went along, tending deserted camps, cooking now and then for a passing crew of rivermen or loggers, growing old in the rough, crude world of the shanty boys—content enough, everybody supposed, just so Will stayed sober.

"Well, we're *glad* to see you, young man," she said. "We heard you was coming."

She poured a cup of coffee from a huge graniteware pot and pushed an array of breads and pastries toward me.

"Have a bite," she urged. "You must be awful hungry. The boys won't be in for more'n an hour yet."

I stirred some sugar into my coffee. It was warm and snug in the kitchen end of the big room. Mrs. Keeler kept up a friendly chatter from behind her vast camp range.

"Suppose you stopped the night at Mrs. Duffy's," she called out.

I said I had.

"I hear the old lady's havin' trouble with her back again."

There followed a lively account of Mrs. Duffy's varied ailments. Then:

"My sister wrote me about that poor Chinaman in Mokoman—he shot himself. . . . Blood all over the shirts and collars . . . Guess he must 'a' been pretty lonesome, maybe . . . so far way from all his folks."

Her talk ranged freely from topic to topic. Nearly all of it was harmless enough gossip about people—the people of her intimate, personal and exceedingly human world—the world of Mokoman and the camps. Only once she ventured abroad a bit, and then it was to mention one who, after all, was like someone you knew.

"Is it true?" she asked, "that Jim Hill is going to dig a canal up to Lake Winnipeg?"

I said I had not known of it.

"Well, I thought maybe you heard something about it

down there—Swan Johnson saw it in the paper. It said Jim Hill was bettin' he'd have his canal to Lake Winnipeg dug before they got done with that one down there in Panama."

She took from the oven a large baking tin of molasses cookies and, shaking it gently, slid the cookies off the open edge onto the table.

"Well, as Swan says," she continued, assuming a broad Scandinavian accent, " 'If Yim Hill say he vill due it, by Yimminy, Yim Hill will due it!' "

She laughed heartily. Her laughter mingled with the sweet, spicy fragrance of the molasses cookies, with the aroma of the coffee, and with the warmth of the wood fire in the camp range. I laughed too, and reached for another doughnut. All these pleasant experiences of the senses were having their sure effect upon my spirits. They made me forget Benson and the rigors of the long ride from Mokoman. I felt less weary and more cheerful. I felt very good, in fact—very content, and looked-after, and at home.

II

The door was flung open, and three men, enveloped in a gust of wintery air, came in from the darkness. One of them was Dempsey, but I did not recognize him at once. He had grown a great red beard. And Dempsey, for his part, paid me no heed at all. He was disputing some point of logging operations with one of his companions.

"Ye and yer goddam dynamite," he growled. "If ye ain't blastin' somethin', Percy, ye ain't happy."

"Saves haulin'," Percy answered laconically.

Dempsey, I noticed, limped badly. He lowered himself heavily to a bench, keeping his right leg out stiffly.

"Cut 'n' fill, that's my system," Percy added. "Cut 'n' fill." He knelt and began to unlace Dempsey's boot, ripping the rawhide thongs through the eyelets with a crackling, whip-lash sound. "Oh, Jennie," he called. "Will ye bring us some soap and water?"

Dempsey's boot came off, and I saw that the gray wool sock inside was dark with blood.

"Saves haulin', maybe," Dempsey conceded. He regarded the sock casually. "But a short haul don't pay best sometimes."

Percy peeled the sock off, slowly and gently. The blade of an ax, obviously, had laid open the foot just above the second joint of the great toe. Smoking tobacco had been packed into the cut to stanch the flow of blood; its brown juice mingled with a little dark fluid still oozing from the wound.

"Lands-a-mercy, what a mess!" Mrs. Keeler slipped a wash basin of warm water under the injured foot. Percy bent close and pressed the wound open with both hands, while Mrs. Keeler sloshed water into it and flushed out the shreds of tobacco. When all was clean, she bandaged up the foot with strips of muslin and, procuring one of the sheepskin shoes that loggers sometimes wore inside their boots, fitted it gingerly over the bandages.

Through all this, Dempsey sat impassively, like a mildly interested, big, red bear. Lumberjacks made a point of bearing pain and hardship stoically; and, although the dressing of the wound must have been painful, Dempsey gave no sign of it.

"Hell," he said wryly when the job was done, "th' cut'll heal up fast enough. But th' boot won't, goddamit!" A laugh rumbled through his beard. His eye fell on me. "Who's this young feller?" he demanded abruptly.

"He's the lad's come up to clerk for you, Paddy," Mrs. Keeler said. "Bradley's boy—son of Jim Bradley."

Dempsey, gazing at me once more over those invisible spectacles of his, sized me up as though I were a stand of pine.

"Ye 're th' clerk, to be sure," he said.

"Yes, sir."

"Aye, I mind now—the clerk." He poked a finger contemplatively into his beard. "And what th' hell will Pat Dempsey be wantin' of a clerk, now?" he asked. "Maybe one of ye can tell me?" He looked about in mock bewilderment.

My face must have shown plainly enough the commingling of amazement, embarrassment and anger that churned up inside of me, because Mrs. Keeler interposed quickly.

"Get along with you, Paddy!" she exclaimed. "Shame on you—alarmin' the poor lad." She waved a bare arm toward the table. "Come on, all of you—*set.*"

Dempsey laughed uproariously, and held out his hand to me.

"Sure, we was only joshin'," he said, including all the others in his joke. "Ye 'r' welcome, to be sure, and it's—" He fixed me suddenly with a severe eye. "How many pounds is there, now, in a bale of hay?" he asked.

"One hundred, sir."

"Kee-rrect!" he shouted. "That," he explained to the others, "is somethin' them college professors never told th' lad. That's somethin' Pat Dempsey had t' tell him. And, by God, he didn't fergit it!"

A pale and vacuous-looking young man, the bull-cook, appeared from somewhere behind the range, opened the cook-shanty door, and gave a few thumps on a dish pan. Benson and several other men, their faces shining and their hair neatly combed, joined us. Mrs. Keeler and the bull-cook brought in food, and with Dempsey sitting at the head of the table, all fell to. The Gordon girl joined us; like the rest, she ate without conversation, according to the etiquette of the camps.

III

"Homesick already?" the Gordon girl asked. She slipped onto the opposite bench and sat facing me across the table.

I looked up from my copy of *Everybody's;* I had been reading Jack London's new serial, *Before Adam.*

"Not exactly," I said. "Why?"

"Well, you kind of looked that way at supper," she said. She took a fragment of cookie from the tin dish and nibbled at it while she regarded me quizzically. "I'm so god-damned tired of euchre," she said.

"I've never played it," I replied. I didn't know what else to say.

She looked over at the after-supper game, under the big hanging lamp nearest the range.

"Well, don't let them get you started," she warned me.

Her voice was husky; her speech, like her movements, slow. How old was she, I wondered. Older than I, by three years—maybe five. By three, I decided—about twenty-two or twenty-three. . . .

"I'm sorry about when you came in," she said. "Guess I wasn't very nice, was I?"

"I didn't notice," I said.

"Well, I didn't mean to be rude—really." She was direct and serious. "But I *was* hoping it would be Ted. And then it just turned out to be you."

"I'm sorry," I said stiffly.

"Ted's my husband," she explained. "You didn't know I was married, did you? Well, I am. Might as well be a widow, though—or an old maid. Ted's been over at Camp Cordy all fall. I ain't seen him for six weeks."

"That's too bad," I said, glancing tentatively at my magazine.

"You're a college boy, ain't you?" It was a statement of fact, not a query. "We heard you were coming—Nick Brady told us last night. What's your name again? Your first name, I mean."

"My name is Matt—Matt Bradley."

"Well, why'd you come here, Matt?" Then, before I could answer. "*I* know what it was."

"Well, if you know—"

"It was a girl. Wasn't it?"

I glared at her, quite speechless. She made a little face of mock surprise at me, then she laughed. Her laugh was low and not very merry; it went along with her husky voice and pouting mouth.

"I wouldn't think you were the type." She studied me brazenly for a moment. "Well, maybe you *are*, at that!"

She was content to let the matter drop. She sat looking at me thoughtfully, taking little bites from the piece of cookie. The steady gaze of her eyes—she seemed to have the same faculty that infants have of keeping them wide open without blinking—was discomposing. I looked away, and I noticed that Mrs. Keeler, holding her cards against her bosom, was looking our way curiously.

"Guess you know what *my* name is," she said casually.

"No," I lied. "Nobody ever told me."

"It's Cherry—Cherry Gordon."

"Well, that's nice. That's a nice name."

"Do you like it?" She looked at me meditatively.

"Sure, I think it's fine."

Cherry shrugged and watched me for a little while.

"Where was you at college?" she asked.

"In Minneapolis—the U."

"Oh. Girls go there too, don't they?"

"Yes."

"I almost went to Minneapolis once—the time my Aunt Minnie was going to have an operation. She died in Mokoman though. We never went. I don't suppose I ever will."

"It's quite a town," I remarked, with an air of experience.

"I wish I *could* see it sometime," Cherry said. "I'd like to see Fort Snelling, and Minnehaha Falls, and the State

Fair and the Glass Block. What I'd like to see most, though, is the shows. Do you ever go?"

"Sometimes."

"To the Orpheum?"

"Yes."

"Did you see *The Chorus Lady*—with Rose Stahl in it?"

"N-no."

"M'lle Modiste?" She pronounced it Millie Modiste.

"No, I didn't see that either. I was pretty busy all the time."

"Well, anyhow, tell me about the city—what's it like down there. You hear the darndest things—"

She began asking questions, interrupting my answers to ask new ones. A torrent of questions, without order or sequence, sometimes unbelievably naïve, sometimes startlingly intuitive. . . . What were the women wearing? Did they actually smoke in public? Had I ever tasted champagne? What was a roof garden like, anyhow—was it really on the roof?

Cherry leaned across the table, intent, excited; a film of perspiration glossed her temples. Sometimes she laughed, a little grimly, at the artlessness of her own queries.

"Never mind if I ask crazy things," she said. "I'm ignorant as hell. I never been *anywheres*."

I searched my mind for small details—the trivia that seemed especially to fascinate Cherry . . . the new Teddy Bears that women were making pets of . . . football night at the Radisson . . . the new peek-a-boo waists . . . the new open-work stockings . . .

The euchre game ended suddenly in a great burst of laughter, and everybody got up. Mrs. Keeler blew out the lamp over the card table and called out to Cherry and me, "Come on, you two."

Cherry merely continued to gaze thoughtfully at me, her mouth formed in a faint, incredulous smile.

"What I can't understand," she said slowly, "is why in hell you ever came to a hole like this."

"It's not so bad, I guess," I said, for want of a better answer.

"Well, I hope," Cherry said, and there was a soft vehemence in her voice, "I hope nobody ever offers to take me out of it."

CHAPTER SIX .

I

*T*HE FOLLOWING EVENING I recorded, in a ruled writing tablet, the first entry in the diary which I kept faithfully throughout the winter of 1906-07. My job as clerk at Camp Dempsey allowed me a good deal of free time for observation of what went on around me, and for putting down my experiences and impressions. This I did with a certain sense of history; because I appreciated, even then, that what I was seeing and living was a chapter of America which would soon be finished, and was never to be repeated. After Mokoman, the old-style lumberjack—the shanty boy who had never seen a steam winch or a shower bath—disappeared forever. After Mokoman there was no more logging in the old, grand manner.

And so, I kept my diary conscientiously, recording everything as accurately and as concretely as I could. The wood-pulp paper of the writing tablet has grown yellow and brittle over these forty years, and must be handled carefully, else it will fall apart. But most of the entries are clearly legible, and perhaps I can best present the personal record of my first days at Camp Tobin with excerpts from some of them.

Rain all day, which this evening has turned to sleet. Stayed inside most of the time. I am quartered in a small log building equipped with two double bunks which used to be the office of Tobin's old camp. Dempsey, Percy Dawson, and a timber cruiser named Shields also sleep here. Keeler keeps a small store of supplies in the building—clothing, tobacco and such.

At daybreak Dawson and Shields went off with Dempsey to the site of this winter's logging operations. I was not asked to go along. The three have been tramping through the woods for a week, Mrs. Keeler says, running roads and figuring out the layout. In about another week the main hauling road will be determined; it will then take about a day apiece to run the branch roads. Soon a crew will come up from Mokoman to build the new camps and cut roads.

There are only about a dozen people here, but the place is populated with innumerable hogs. This morning, as I stepped out of the door in the darkness, a very large one scrambled from under my feet with such terrific squeals that I was scared half to death. Temperature at noon, 42 degrees.

October 27th

I have had a bad case of "the blues" ever since arriving here. Maybe it is the weather—still dark and rainy. Or maybe I am homesick!

Dempsey and the other men are friendly enough, but they say very little to me. I seem to have no duties, and it is too wet outside for any exploring. So I have stuck close to the stove all day, reading old newspapers.

I see by a month-old paper that race riots are still spreading in the South. Ten Negroes were lynched in Atlanta in one day, and two the next. Some were burned at the stake. I have been trying to imagine what kind of people would do such a thing.

A wet snow has just begun to fall. The flakes are so big, and the fall is so heavy, that I can't see the buildings across the road. Temperature at 1 P.M., 34 degrees.

October 28th

Today is Sunday, and raining besides, so nobody did any work, except Mrs. Keeler and the bull-cook, of course. Their work is never done.

Dempsey and Dawson spent the afternoon discussing the size of crew they will need this winter. Or, rather, arguing about it. They wrangle constantly. Dempsey shouts a lot and after a while Dawson shuts up and won't say *anything*—which infuriates Dempsey.

They had a hot one this evening over Dan Patch's time, when he set the world's record last fall. Dempsey said 1:55¼ and Percy said 1:55½. It occurred to me to look it up in the *World Almanac,* and when it turned out that Dempsey was right, he was very pleased with me and made quite a little speech on the value of a college education.

Cherry Gordon wore a skirt and high-heeled shoes today, on account of it being Sunday, and had her hair done up in a pompadour and braids.

Dempsey invited me to go along with him and Dawson today (Shields has gone back to town). Mrs. Keeler put up a lunch of sandwiches and doughnuts for us, and we struck off immediately after breakfast. We walked in the morning twilight for almost an hour, on an old logging road that twisted through the slashings; then we came to timber and the site of Dempsey's new camps.

Dempsey plans to log six forties, or 240 acres of timberland, this winter. That is about the area of a good-sized farm. The land has already been cruised. It is estimated that around six million feet of timber can be cut here this season, which is about average. Four to six million feet is a good cut, and not many camps have ever put in more than ten million.

The timber is white and Norway pine, mostly. About 80 per cent white pine, Dawson says. It is scattered in bunches—sometimes in thin stands; sometimes a million feet, perhaps, in a bunch. Spruce, tamarack, and some birch and poplar are mixed in.

We arrived back at camp after dark, all soaked (it has begun to drizzle again) and I, at least, very tired. Dempsey, in spite of himself, limped badly on his injured foot. We had venison for supper which Mrs. Keeller, much to Dempsey's disgust, stewed instead of roasted.

Out again with Dempsey and Dawson today. Benson came in with the mail, but nothing for me. I don't feel very well this evening. Think I'll turn in now.

Mrs. Keeler brought me some Sanford's Ginger Tea in a china cup.

"Drink this, now," she said. "It'll fix you up. It'll fix you up fine."

But the chills had me shaking so badly that I couldn't manage the cup, so Mrs. Keeler held it for me while I tried to swallow the hot, gagging brew. She placed extra blankets on me, but they only weighed on my aching body without warming me. Nothing could warm me. The blankets couldn't, nor the ginger tea, nor the stove, although it glowed red-hot on the under side of its cast-iron belly.

Mrs. Keeler placed her rough, cold hand for a moment on my forehead. "I'll be back soon's the bread's out of the oven," she said. "If you have to get up—use the bucket on the floor there."

I was sick for almost a week—not dangerously sick, I guess, but feeling pretty bad. I must have been delirious for a while, because there are a couple of days near the beginning that I cannot account for. The next I remember was waking up, soggy with perspiration, and very thirsty, and wondering why the lamp was lit, since it was night and everybody was asleep.

When I sat up and tried to pull off some of the blankets, somebody climbed out of the lower bunk across the room. It wasn't Dempsey, as I expected. It was Mrs. Keeler in her big, flannel nightgown. She padded over to me.

"What's the matter?" I asked. "What's the trouble?"

"Sh-h-h—nothing's the matter, son," Mrs. Keeler said. "Everything's fine. . . . And how do you feel now?" She pushed me gently back on my pillow.

"I feel all right," I said. I was vaguely surprised to hear my own voice so small and weak. "I feel fine."

Mrs. Keeler felt my forehead, pushed back my damp hair. She stood looking at me for a little while, without saying anything. Then she started to cry. She didn't sob or make any great ado; she just stood there with the tears on her face and kept repeating, "Thank God! Well, thank God!"

The next evening Dempsey and Dawson moved back into the cabin with me.

"If ye're through sleepin' with Jennie," Dempsey said, "might we be havin' the use of our bunks again?"

Five times a day Mrs. Keeler gave me food—at each regular meal time, and again in mid-morning and mid-afternoon: soup, oatmeal, boiled rice, toast and tea. Sometimes she brought it over herself, but generally she sent Cherry with the tray.

It was like being in a hospital, almost, with two nurses. Lying comfortably in my blankets, I wondered how I would have fared in my sickness if it hadn't been for Mrs. Keeler. What did the men in the camps do when they became seriously ill? You hardly ever heard of a man dying in the woods, unless he were killed in an accident. But they must have fallen sick too. Even with my own father in the woods so much, I hadn't thought about it before. But no doubt my mother had.

Cherry would sometimes visit with me while I ate my food. As I grew stronger, she might remain for an hour at a time—sitting on a chair tilted back against the corner post of Dempsey's bunk, or maybe stretched out on the bunk itself.

"Ma says not to pester you with a lot of fool questions," she said. "But you don't mind my talkin', do you?"

I didn't at all. Her conversation was mostly about the camps—scraps of news that had trickled in—gossip that had come her way—reports on Dempsey's progress. It was lively and entertaining, and it helped to pass the long, monotonous days of my convalescence. Sometimes, also, Cherry read to me, mostly from old newspapers.

And so I got the news, at least a month old. Dr. Cook had climbed Mt. McKinley—he hadn't—he had. Buffalo Bill had returned home from Europe with sixty Sioux. Mt. Pelee had erupted again. The Chicago Nationals had taken the championship from the Chicago Americans in a great pitching duel between Altrock and Brown. And the Thaw trial was dragging on. . . .

"It says here that today's farm girl is wearing high-heeled shoes and picture hats and peek-a-boo waists (maybe a little more peek-a-boo than her city cousins, it says) and three-story gloves. . . ." She struck a sort of burlesque Anna Held pose, "Coax me," she smirked, "come on and coax me!"

Cherry went to the window, rubbed a clear space in the ice and peered out for a little while.

"Still snowing," she said. "Maybe Ted's coming in to-morrow."

"How long since you've seen him?"

"I told you. Six weeks—almost seven now. He's helping to put up Cordy's new camps over on the Moosehorn. It's hard for him to get over here."

She said this a little defensively.

"He gets to Mokoman once in a while, though," she said reflectively. "He's probably got a girl there." She laughed, but it was a mirthless laugh. "If I thought Ted was two-timin' me," she said slowly, "while I'm stuck up here in this profane hole—"

She used a shocking word that not even the loggers resorted to very often.

"Well, what are you gawking at?" she demanded. "You needn't act so goddamned innocent!"

When she opened the door to leave, the snow blew across the room and pelted my face. I caught a glimpse of a swirling white world outside. It had been snowing steadily for two days, and now the wind was rising to almost blizzard force.

III

The year 1906 brought down upon Minnesota the heaviest snows since '96. In the north there was a fall of thirty inches on the ground by mid-January—which meant, of course, drifts to the very eaves of many houses. And in the vast "snow belt," several miles wide and running north from the head of the lake for an unknown distance, the depth was even greater. Tobin's camp was in this belt.

When, for the first time in almost a week, I again stepped outdoors, it was into a world that had magically, incredibly transformed itself. All my life I had seen snow —but never quite so *suddenly* as this. And seldom so much of it.

The bull-cook, shoveling out a path from the cook-house to the creek, was a frantic mite struggling against a dazzling universe of white. Whiteness that lay in solid paraboloidal planes upon the ground, in great thick slabs upon the roofs, in heaps that weighted down the spruce and balsams. The bull-cook carved out chunks of white-ness with his shovel, tossed them into the air. And the wind, which had not yet quite died down, filled the cold, blue atmosphere with crystalline particles all about him.

Perhaps because I was still a little weak from my sick-ness, it was quite a struggle for me to get through the big drifts to the cook-house. And the cup of hot coffee that Mrs. Keeler poured for me was very welcome.

"Indeed, it's good to see you back on your feet again," she said. "And a great relief to me, too."

She was making cinnamon rolls on the big pine work table by the window. I watched hungrily as she rolled out a large, soft pad of dough, buttered it, and sprinkled it thickly with cinnamon and sugar. She formed the pad into a long cylinder, pinching the edges into place; then she sliced it—each slice a beautiful, glossy spiral of spicy brown and creamy white—and tucked the sections snugly side by side in a baking tin.

"I was scared there—when you was talkin' wild," she

said. "Makes me feel funny—kind of funny inside—to hear folks talkin' out of their head. It's *eerie*."

Mrs. Keeler placed the rolls in the oven and added a couple of sticks of wood to the fire.

"It just shows how close everybody is to bein' crazy," she said seriously. "Don't take no more'n a little touch of fever. You was pickin' blueberries all night once. Bushels of 'em!"

She laughed, but I wondered how deep her laughter went, for she was gravely silent for a little while. Then she added, without smiling, "Most camp watchers are a little touched."

"Well, who isn't?" I asked, trying feebly to lighten the conversation.

"The first big snow's the worst," Mrs. Keeler said, exactly as though we had been discussing the weather. "That's the worst. It makes you feel kind of funny—funny inside, like I said. Look at this place, now. Nobody can get in—nobody can get out. We're stuck here for sure . . . Specially at night, I still get kind of scared sometimes—same's I used to when Will and me first came up. Sometimes I feel like I want to get out and run down the road—or scream—or something . . ."

She looked at me with a sort of shy, surprised look, as though perplexed by her own spoken words.

"Ain't that silly?" she asked. "Can't help it, though. It's been the same for eighteen, twenty years." She changed the subject with a gesture toward the big window over the work table. "Will you look at that, now!"

The snow had piled up solidly, halfway to the top of

the glass; the panes made a clean-cut cross-section of the great drift outside. It was as if the snow were pressing to come in. And beyond the window, above the snow, there was nothing but the glinting winter sky.

"Cherry said Benson's due in today," I said. "Can he make it through this snow?"

"Oh, he'll make it, all right. It'll take a lot of swearin' maybe, but Ed'll get through."

He didn't get through, however—not that day, nor the next. Neither Benson arrived, nor the crew that was expected up—and already overdue—to build the camps. Dempsey tramped about on his snowshoes, argued with Percy, grumbled impatiently. Mrs. Keeler grew alarmed.

"D'you figure something might of happened to him, Paddy?" she asked anxiously.

"About that I don't know, Jennie," said Dempsey irritably, "and about that I don't give a damn. But where th' hell's them men?"

After we had turned in that night, however, I heard him call drowsily from his bunk, "Percy—if Ed don't show up by mornin', guess we better wheel down th' road a ways and find out what th' hell's detainin' him."

IV

But they all came in during the night—Benson and about a dozen men who had followed the tote-team's trail over the drifted roads.

It had taken them four days from Mokoman—twice the usual time. The snow wasn't as deep lower down, Benson said; the blizzard hadn't caught them until after they had left Mrs. Duffy's. But from then on conditions could be described only in his strongest terms.

"Hell, it wasn't so bad," drawled a voice from the other side of the bunkhouse stove. "I mind th' time I was up fer Terry O'Sullivan. It was durin' th' winter of '88 and th' snow was so deep we was cuttin' ten-foot stumps on th' Lazy Jack—"

I craned my neck to see who the speaker was. Sure enough, it was the Whiteface Liar.

CHAPTER SEVEN

I

Camp Dempsey
November 17, 1906

Dear Ma:

Ed Benson (he's the tote-teamster) brought in your letter this morning, and I am happy to hear that you and Carlie are well and everything is fine at home.

That leaves "the Whole Dam Family" in good shape, I guess, because I have got over the little sickness I wrote you about, and I am now feeling fine. I am also very busy. Maybe you and Carlie would like to know what I am doing to keep myself out of mischief.

Well, for the past two weeks we have been building our new camps over on Wolf Creek. We really got started on the sixth, right after the big storm. We hitched six horses to Camp Tobin's old snow plow—four in front and two behind—and cleared out the road to the new camp site. A crew of swampers was already down there, cutting the skidding trails and clearing brush.

About a dozen men—all expert sawyers, horse-skinners, and axmen—then got busy on the actual building of the camps. Soon half a dozen more men and some horses came in. As the men arrived, Dempsey sent them over to me and I put their names down in the camp books. They are old timers, mostly, and regular followers of Dempsey's. You know some of them, Ma—Jack Leonard, Tom Donnely, Donald McShane, Pat Dolan, Homer Stapleton, and the Whiteface Liar you often heard Pa speak of. Some of them were pretty seedy looking. Too much celebration on the Point before coming up, I guess!

The sawyers started on the Norway pine on the eighth, and the woods echoed to the shout of "Timber-rrr!" as the big trees came down. They were trimmed and cut full-length.

The deep snow hampered the men at first. You never saw such snow, Ma! The sawyers had to shovel out around each tree—else they would have left ten-foot stumps! Dangling Dailey (who is quite a weather prophet) says it's going to be a cold winter as well as a snowy one. He says the fish in Loon Lake are growing fur—and that proves it.

By the tenth the walls of the bunkhouse were up. It is seventy-five feet long and thirty feet wide, and it is built entirely of full-length Norway pine logs. The logs were notched at each end, so as to lock together at the corners. They were then slid up four poles and settled into place. It is amazing how accurately the "corner men" can notch these logs, so as to make strong, tight joints.

The walls were then chinked with long V-shaped strips of wood, which were pounded tightly into the spaces between the logs and then plastered over with mud. On the inside, swamp moss was packed into the cracks. I helped gather the moss, and it was no fun!

The roof of the bunkhouse is made of sawn lumber, brought up from Mokoman. The boards are nailed to a spruce pole framework and covered with tar paper. The floor is also made of boards.

The bunkhouse is very clean and new-looking and smells strongly of tar paper and fresh-cut lumber. Without bunks, stoves, or anybody in it, its size seemed enormous—reminded me of the roller skating rink on Sixth Street.

While the bunkhouse was going up, the men were working on the other camps, of course, and also on the roads. The other buildings are: the cook-shanty (which is about the same size as the bunkhouse), the barn, the office, and some other small buildings. The last thing to be done was the smith's forge, which was put up yesterday afternoon. It is built of rocks and mortar, and with the temperature down around zero, it was *some* job. The ranges have also been put up in the cook-shanty, and the stoves are in place in the other buildings.

Everybody agrees that we have a very tidy set of well-built camps—which, they say, is always true of one of Dempsey's layouts. Dempsey has announced that we are moving on the nineteenth—day after tomorrow—and I, for one, won't be sorry to get out of the old camp we have been in since October. It is too well *inhabited*—if you know what I mean.

Well, there isn't much other news, Ma. Mr. Keeler (they call him "Big Bill") gave us a concert in the cook-house last Sunday. He played his talking machine, and we listened until supper time to some coon songs, "Uncle

Josh," "Clarence the Copper," some band records, and three times to "The Letter Edged in Black."

Mrs. Keeler, poor soul, does her best to keep everybody well-fed and happy, but she has her troubles. One of them is a willing but not very bright Swede named Swan Swanson, who is helping her out as cookee. Dempsey says he hears the county is offering a bounty on Swedes this year, and Mrs. Keeler ought to collect on Swan.

Mrs. Keeler, by the way, sends you her regards. She says that, although she has never met you, she feels that she knows you. She is an awfully nice woman, Ma. I hope you meet her sometime in Mokoman.

Well, I guess that's about all for this time, Ma. I hope Carlie is doing his chores (how about it, Carlie?) and you are taking good care of yourself. I'll write again real soon.

With love,

Matt.

II

So we built Pat Dempsey's main camps in two weeks by the calendar, with a crew of twenty men, and we were eating our beans in the cook-house on the twentieth of November, well pleased with the job we had done.

For Camp Dempsey was a tight, snug set of camps, you had to admit, and properly laid out. On three sides—the south, east and west—it was well protected against the weather by a stand of Norway pine; on the north it was sheltered by a high, thinly-wooded ridge. As you came onto it at the top of the hill, where the road crossed over the ridge, and saw it down there in the pine woods, it looked for all the world like one of those models you sometimes see in museums—very neat and orderly, with the camp rubbish covered by the smooth, clean snow, and the smoke from the fires going straight up on still days.

The buildings, which were six in number, were set low in the snow; and they huddled close together, as if for companionship in the lonely forest. All were disposed in trim rows along the two sides of a sort of "company street."

The main camps, so as to be handy to water, occupied the north side of the street, opening their back doors to Wolf Creek. They were: the bunkhouse, where the men lived and slept; the cook-shanty, where they ate; and, somewhat removed, the horse barns which sheltered Camp Dempsey's draft animals. Opposite these buildings were three smaller ones: the office, the filer's shack, and the blacksmith's shop. A roothouse had been sunk into the hillside just west of the office, and a sheltered latrine had been dug a sanitary hundred feet or so beyond the smith's.

And that, excepting the pig pen and a storage shed or two, was all of Dempsey's camp—all that you could see, at any rate, as you came upon it on the tote-road over the ridge. Save for those columns of smoke going up from the chimneys, it would appear to be quite deserted. There would be no sound, most likely, barring an occasional muffled thump from the interior of the barn, or the faint clang of metal in the smith's shop. And there would be no visible sign of life either, unless the barn door should open with a great outpouring of steam, and you should see the barn-boss scuttling through the cold to the cook-shanty for a cup of coffee.

Yet Dempsey's camp was the home of almost a hundred men during the long, snowy winter of 1906; and many things, good and bad, happened there, as you would expect, in the hundred and twenty days that we were "up for Dempsey."

III

Moving day started off with the rather startling spectacle of an empty feed sack propelling itself with energetic leaps and bounds out of the cook-shanty door. The sack, after plunging erratically over the snow, sprang directly at Diddy Dupre, who was stooped over in the darkness, tying up a bundle of peavey handles. Diddy, understandably alarmed, let out a terrified shriek and dived for the security of the nearest camp. The sack then capered madly away in the opposite direction with Swan, the new cookee, in earnest pursuit. It contained the cook-house cat.

For me the transfer to Dempsey's new camp held a certain excitement and promise of adventure. And this feeling, I think, was shared in some degree at least by the others—even by Dempsey; for there was a certain bustle and gaiety about the place on moving morning that seemed to mark the moment as a special one.

As for those who were being left behind—Jennie and Big Bill Keeler and Cherry Gordon—I suppose their emotions were quite the opposite. For them it must have been depressing to see the life and activity, the talk and sound and smell of people, depart, leaving the three of them alone once more to the emptiness of Tobin's old camp and the long winter.

Cherry, obviously enough, reflected such a state of mind when she came into the office where I was checking my inventory. She went over to the stove and stood close to it, warming her backside.

"Well," she said, "I guess we won't see much of *you* any more."

"I guess not," I said. "Expect I'll be pretty busy over at Dempsey's."

"Well—come to see us when you can. Whenever you can come, we'll be glad to see you. Ma will, especially. . . ."

She rubbed the backs of her hands against the seat of her denims, slowly up and down.

"I'm *worried* about Ma," she said suddenly.

"What's the matter?" I asked, absent-mindedly concerned. "Isn't she well?"

"Oh, she's all right. She's all right, I guess. It's just the way she talks. She's beginnin' to talk funny. About greens. Keeps talkin' about greens all the time. . . ."

Cherry looked at me with her steady, contemplative gaze.

"Maybe that ain't so funny," she said. "Maybe it's me that's nuts."

"Guess we all get a hankering this time of year—" I began, but Cherry wasn't listening.

"Then there's that song," she said. "Ever hear Ma sing it? Well—it *scares* me."

76

"Song? What song?"

"Ma's been eighteen years—summer and winter—in these lousy camps," she continued. "Her and Pa—all by theirselves, mostly."

She wasn't listening to me, I knew. She'd forgotten I was there—I and my inventory and my eager interest in the affairs of our moving.

"Ma's *got* to put up with it, I guess," she said, her voice low and husky. "But, by Christ, *I* don't."

Suddenly she held out her hand, hot from the stove's heat, and gave mine a strong, quick clasp.

"Well, so long," she said. "Don't forget to come and see us."

At the door she paused for a moment, as though she were about to add something more; but whatever it might have been, she left, quite abruptly, without having said it.

A short time later I told Mrs. Keeler and Big Bill good-by, and left Camp Tobin atop a load of hay and feed. Mrs. Keeler and her husband came to the cook-house door and stood for a little while in the bitter cold, watching us as we drove away. I looked for Cherry, but she wasn't with them.

IV

At five o'clock on the morning of November 19 while the stars were still dancing with cold brilliance in the winter sky, I was roused from my sleep by the rolling notes of the shanty boss's "gabrel." I climbed out of my bunk, confused for a moment by my new surroundings, and began my new life as the clerk of Dempsey's camp.

77

Perhaps at this point I should mention my duties as camp clerk, and describe briefly the quarters which for the next three months or so were to be not only my home, but camp headquarters and wannigan for the crew.

We lived—Dempsey, the scaler and I—in the comparative luxury of the camp "office," a beautifully constructed cabin, tight, clean, free from bedbugs and graybacks, and altogether a fit abode for a great woods boss and his immediate entourage.

It was a simple building, however, and simple to describe. You can imagine it, I am sure, quite as plainly as I myself can recall its details: a low log structure, perhaps fourteen feet square, and made proof against the weather with wooden caulking strips and mud mortar; a door and square window facing the camp street, another window in the western wall. The rear corners of the room were occupied by double-deck bunks, built of sawn lumber and wide enough to accommodate two sleepers. A long, low cast-iron stove, set in a shallow box filled with sand, radiated its genial warmth from the center of the floor. And that is all, except for two chairs, and the van or wannigan.

Yet, of course, that is *not* all; that is nothing, really, except what your two eyes would see as you came into the office to ask Dempsey, perhaps, for another peavey man on the landing. In what I have just described there is nothing of the feeling it would give you to lie warm and dry in your blankets, with a shrieking blizzard battering at the stout walls of your cabin, and the wind thundering in the pines; or to sit by the stove of a deadly still night, so cold that the very stars crackled in the sky, and soak up the heat of a panting birch log fire; or to look out of your window on a frosty day, through a wall of icicles as thick as your leg and extending like stalactites in a cave from eaves to ground, and yourself as snug as the camp cat beside the cook-house range.

Besides serving as living quarters for Dempsey, the scaler and me, the office, as I have said, also housed the wannigan. This was the corner where I kept the camp store and performed my simple paper work. It was at your right as you entered, and was separated from the rest of the room by a deal counter. Shelves against the back wall held my small stock of merchandise; a wider shelf under the window was my desk and work table; and a large kerosene lamp hanging over the counter illuminated, although but dimly, the entire room.

The most spectacular item in the wannigan—which comprised chiefly work clothes, tobacco, and miscellaneous articles such as pipes, pencils and writing tablets—was Hinckley's Bone Liniment. The label on the bottle indicated that this esteemed remedy—standard throughout the woods—was "good for man or beast." A few drops, like absinthe, turned a dipper of water into a milky fluid which gave off choking fumes. It was reputed to possess great therapeutic value in the treatment of chills, colds and hangovers.

The wannigan also offered the ailing lumberjack such sterling remedies as Dr. Perry Davis' Painkiller and White Pine and Balsam Cough Syrup. Dempsey's rugged crew, like all loggers, was given to various aches and complaints

—brought on, no doubt, by perspiring in arctic temperatures—and the demands on our simple dispensary were heavy. Against more serious illnesses, or accidents, we had nothing in the way of sterile bandages, antiseptics or narcotics, even though the nearest doctor was two days away.

Tobacco, the logger's only luxury and solace, was naturally an important item of the wannigan. We carried three brands of smoking tobacco, Peerless, Standard and Home Made. They were the smoke of strong men and came packed in paper bags. (The era of smoking tobacco in tins arrived almost a decade later and, it has been noted, coincided roughly with the final disappearance of the true shanty boy or timber beast in the Great Lakes region.)

Customarily these tobaccos were smoked in the "nose warmer," a type of briar pipe peculiar to the woods, with a short stem which kept the bowl not more than two inches from the smoker's proboscis, and undoubtedly served some utilitarian purpose in cold weather; they could and did, however, double as "eating" tobacco. There were no cigarettes at Camp Dempsey, nor papers in which to roll your own. Dempsey, like most boss loggers of his epoch, disapproved of the "pimp sticks"; he fired on sight anyone caught smoking them.

In the line of straight chewing tobaccos we had Climax and Spearhead. They came in long, sweet-smelling slabs, packed in little wooden boxes, which I sold by the pound or cut into individual plugs by means of a sort of miniature guillotine. And for the Swedes and Finns, who more and more frequently were beginning to appear in the camps, we always carried a fresh supply of Copenhagen

Snuff, commonly referred to as "snoose," and sometimes jocosely called Scandinavian dynamite or Swedish breakfast food.

"Give me enough Swedes and snuff," said James J. Hill, "and I'll build a railroad to hell." "Don't ever run out of snuff," said Dempsey. "I'd as lief run out of timber." We were careful always to have a fresh stock on hand.

In addition to tending the camp store, it was my duty as camp clerk to requisition supplies: food for the cook, hay and feed for the barn-boss, round and flat iron and charcoal for the smith. Also, I kept the crew's "time" and swept out the office every morning after breakfast. On occasion I wrote letters for Dempsey. I also saw to it that he did not set himself on fire at bedtime; for it was Dempsey's habit to have a smoke in bed in the evening, and often he fell asleep with his pipe burning vigorously. When this happened, I would carefully remove the pipe from his mouth and deposit it in some less inflammable place than a hay-filled bunk.

V

It was a pleasant feeling, after I had unpacked my little stock of merchandise, to see it arranged in orderly piles upon the shelves. It gave a "settled" look to the office. I was established in my job, at last, and the wannigan was open for business.

One of my first customers, unfortunately, was a swamper named Joe Gachot. I had disliked him from the start—if for no other reason than his foul mouth, and his habit of breaking wind, then smiling as though he had done something clever and funny. On his first night in camp he had tried to get the other men to join him in guying me for a greenhorn; when they guyed him instead, he made no effort to conceal his resentment against me. Incidentally, as I put Joe Gachot's name down in the camp books, I had a strong feeling that I had seen him somewhere before.

On the day after moving, Joe had been "laying in" with a cold, but he felt well enough to pay me a mid-afternoon visit, when almost no one else was in camp. He shuffled into the office and cast his piggish little eyes over my small stock of woods clothing.

"Lemme see one of them shirts, clerk," he said, without preliminary greeting.

I took down a plaid woolen shirt and laid it before him on the counter. Gachot examined it casually, then pushed it away with a vague air of disapproval.

"Let's see some mitts."

He examined them in the same leisurely and faintly contemptuous manner.

"Sox."

Item by item Gachot went over everything I had to show him, saying nothing at all, but turning now and then to direct a spurt of tobacco juice at the sand box under the stove. For perhaps half an hour he amused himself in this fashion; then he turned his attention to the tobacco shelf.

"Gimme some Nigger Hair," he said.

I thought he was trying to guy me; at that time I was

not aware that a brand of tobacco, cut in fine strips, black and curly, and actually called Nigger Hair, was on the market.

"We don't have any," I said shortly.

Gachot managed to look at once perplexed and aggrieved.

"Whatcha mean, ya ain't got any?" he asked softly.

"We've just got Standard and Peerless," I said, "and Hand Made."

"My smoke's Nigger Hair." Gachot leaned confidentially on the counter. " Listen, clerk—if ya want t' be pop'lar round here, maybe you better kinda—you know—pay a little 'tention to what th' *boys* wants."

He studied me as though, I thought, he were trying to place me in his memory.

"Well, gimme some of yer lousy Peerless," he said.

I don't know whether Gachot actually smelled bad, but it seemed to me that he left an unpleasant odor behind him in the office.

CHAPTER EIGHT

I

BLACK JACK CORRIGAN came into camp the day after we had moved, and I put his name down in the books: John C. Corrigan, landing. He was a good man in the woods, a great one on the drive. It was said of him, "Jack could waltz across a chocolate cake in his corked boots and never scratch the frosting." He had been with Dempsey for seven winters.

On the same day Jake McCloskey appeared on the "pike," as the tote-road into camp was called; he paused at the edge of the clearing and, after properly lubricating his larynx, announced his arrival with a series of frightening yells. He was the same Jake McCloskey who caused the riot in Eau Pleine at the St. Patrick's day dance in '03, when he demanded "The Protestant Boys" of the fiddlers; and the one who climbed a telephone pole during the Firemen's Convention in Mokoman and scattered handfuls of quarters, with appropriate whoops and yells, to the crowd below. He would be a first-rate four-horse teamster when he had sobered up.

Also, toward evening, arrived Sandy MacDonald, a wiry man, loud and brisk of voice and nimble of feet, as a good sky-hooker had to be. He wore the reserved, professional air becoming to a man who could, without trying too hard, put 10,000 feet of logs on a hauling sleigh. On the books he was Douglas MacDonald, top loader.

The crew was building up swiftly now. It was good weather for sawing, despite the deep snow, and we should be hauling by the tenth of December, Dempsey said. All week long, new men continued to arrive—first sawyers, undercutters, skidders, swampers, skidway men. Later would come the loaders, landing men, hauling teamsters, road monkeys, icers.

Many of the names I entered in my books were well and widely known in the Mokoman timber country: Dangling Dailey, a boss logger himself until the drink had caught up with him; Jake Le Breche, the great half-breed birler; Crosshaul Carlson, who was reputed to be able to converse with horses; the Galloping Twins, whose specialty was road icing, and who were always hired—or fired—together; and Paddy Miles, whose name was really John Lanigan, but who was called Paddy Miles by everyone because of a song he sang—"Paddy Miles the Irish Boy." Almost every member of the crew knew all the others; almost all of them had been up for Dempsey before, some of them many times.

For the most part they were men—they and their fathers before them—who had followed the white pine clean across the continent. They came from Wisconsin recently —from Chippewa Falls and Eau Claire and Wausau; before that, from Michigan—Saginaw, Bay City, Muskegon; and even farther back, from Bangor and the Penobscot, and Three Rivers in Quebec. Soon they were to take two more great leaps, one to the white pine of Idaho, and then another—and their last—to the colossal fir and spruce forests of Oregon and Washington. Finally, in an alien atmosphere of electric lights, shower baths and movie theatres, the breed was destined quietly to go down, its back against the sea and bewilderment in its eyes.

But in 1906 there was still plenty of pine in Minnesota, and the crew now gathering at Dempsey's camp to cut it differed only in minor ways from the shanty boys and white-water men of an earlier but scarcely cruder day. Fully two-thirds of them were Scotch or Irish, of the old red-sashed, bull-whacking stock. A few were French-Canadians, all from the Three Rivers country. There were half a dozen Swedes, a couple of Indians, a lone Finn, and, for a short time, Roothouse Pete, whose origins, like everything else about him, were mysterious.

They were a sinewy, hard-bitten lot, whose stagged Mac-Millan pants hung loosely around their flat bellies. They were "able" men, all of them; but none so able as Dempsey himself who once, on some occasion or other that seemed to call for a vote of confidence, had stomped into the bunkhouse and announced: "I can lick any son-of-a-bitch and his brother in this here shanty." Nobody had cared to dispute him.

II

The Whiteface Liar claimed that bedbugs have a way of knowing when a logging crew is about to move from an old camp to a new one, and usually make the move a day or two ahead of the men. "Takes 'em longer t' make the trip," he explained. He said, furthermore, that on the day before we transferred from Camp Tobin, he had observed long lines of the little beasts winding through the woods toward Dempsey's new camps, although the intelligent ones simply stowed away in the camp blankets and hitch-hiked their way over. It did appear that a reception committee, at least, was at the new bunkhouse to welcome us. And within a few days Camp Dempsey, for all its brand-newness, had its full complement, not only of bedbugs, but of camp lice as well.

For some obscure reason, the presence of vermin in a lumberjack's living quarters, together with other unpleasant and unsanitary aspects of his winter's lodgings, has always been regarded humorously—and especially by the lumberjacks themselves. Yet, looked at objectively, it is a little difficult to see the light side of a fetid, over-heated, vermin-ridden bunkhouse—even a new and well-constructed one, such as we had at Dempsey's camp.

Had you been a swamper or horse-skinner, let us say, you would have trudged home at night to a sleeping camp which was typical, I believe, of the bunkhouse in any well-conducted logging camp of the period. And, unless you were a hardened timber-beast, you would have found it pretty rugged.

Our bunkhouse was built, I think I have already recorded, of Norway pine logs, eight high. On one side were twenty-two bunks, on the other twenty-one; the odd space was occupied by a sink where the crew washed up.

At one time bunks were built "shot-gun" style, at right

angles to the wall, and you crawled in over the end. But those at Dempsey's camp were of the more modern type and were built in two tiers (upper and lower bunks) parallel to the side walls of the building. Each bunk was wide enough to sleep two men. You strewed some hay over the bottom poles, stretched a blanket over the hay, put up a little shelf to hold your personal belongings, tacked a few pictures from the *Police Gazette* on the wall, and called it home.

Perhaps because they got so much of it during the day, all lumberjacks mortally feared and hated fresh air, and bunkhouses were scientifically constructed to keep it in its proper place—outside. The only means of ventilating ours was a small skylight near each end of the roof (the windows in the gables were for light only). These skylights were hinged, but they were opened, if at all, only with the utmost caution. For the most part, the heat from the big barrel stove, stoked with four-foot birch logs and ordinarily fired to a dull red glow, remained inside. And the cold—along with all fresh air—was successfully shut out.

The result was appalling. There are three smells—all of them unpleasant, unfortunately—which, I think, I shall carry forever in my nostrils: the smell of the *souks* in Fez; the smell of the Chicago stockyards in the dead heat of a mid-September day; and the smell of our bunkhouse at night, with the stovepipe a cherry red in the darkness, and the crew giving off with alarming sounds of strangulation from each of the forty-three bunks. Or, if not forever, I am sure that I shall remember our bunkhouse odor the longest.

It was an odor composed of many elements. The most powerful component was, perhaps, eighty-odd pairs of wet socks, hung on long poles to dry over the stove. But seldom washed underwear and never washed bodies contributed richly; so did blankets that were never aired, hay that remained in the bunks all winter, tobacco juice in the floor boards, barn smells brought in by the teamsters, and the smoke of villainous tobacco. Finally, there was the noisome air itself, breathed and re-breathed by almost a hundred men.

That is what our bunkhouse smelled of; but it is not *how* it smelled. Only experience itself could convey the effect of this commingling, this ageing-together of odors. It was not amusing—it was staggering. And yet, the crew, long inured, were quite unmindful of it all; but then, they were also unmindful of the bedbugs and the lice.

In such an atmosphere the people at Dempsey's camp slept and spent their leisure hours.

At night, stupid and drowsy from a long day of toil in the open air and from the soporific effects of a heavy meal, they sat on the deacon seat, a long bench running down both sides of the camp for its entire length, and whiled away the short interval between supper and lights out. The teamsters took care of their horses, some of the men ground their axes, but mostly the time was passed in talking and smoking, until at nine o'clock the bull-cook blew out the hanging kerosene lamps, and Dempsey's camp went soundly—if not quietly—to sleep.

III

Joe Lavoie arrived in camp between two days. By the dim light of the tote-teamster's lantern he was unloaded from a sleigh full of hay and feed and, with great secrecy, he remained for three days and nights, perspiring heroically. On the morning of the fourth day he put on a clean white shirt and, never inquiring how he happened to have come to Dempsey's, took over in the cook-shanty where he officiated, dead sober, until camp broke in the spring.

The circumstances surrounding Joe's strange induction as cook at Dempsey's camp were these.

For several weeks all had not been going well in the cook-shanty; and of a logging camp few observations of more serious import could be made. For it was difficult to over-emphasize the importance of the logging camp cook. He was by far the highest paid member of the crew, worth two top loaders or three good sawyers. He could make or break a camp, as every boss logger knew—and none better than Dempsey.

So it was a matter of concern to Dempsey when he first began to suspect that the beans were a little difficult for even a swamper's digestive tract, and that the Larrigan pie was not everything it could be. His worries mounted as a few of the crew began to grumble about "boilers" and "hardtack outfits." And they reached a climax when Old Alec Mackenzie announced that we had "the best danged cook south of Fifty-nine."

For Old Alec always said the opposite of what he meant;

he was a peculiar and contrary man. For more years than anybody could tell, he had been cruising timber in the Minnesota and Wisconsin pine lands: "Since two years before Columbus," according to the landing-boss. He had paced section lines so long that he counted automatically, it was said, even when he strolled the city streets; and he could find a corner post by smell. A better cruiser, all agreed, had never cussed a compass man, and perhaps none as good.

But Alec Mackenzie was peculiar and perverse, and he regarded all logging camps with a certain distaste. Perhaps it was with the envy of a man who must spend his nights in lonely cruisers' tents and eat his bannock beside a solitary fire; perhaps a species of contempt for all who lived in sheltered luxury; or perhaps, as most held, merely the pure cussedness of the old man's nature. Whatever the cause, he was a sour and perverse man, sure enough— and yet, well liked and respected. And no woods boss regarded lightly Old Alec Mackenzie's appraisal of his camp, his crew, his cook—or himself.

Dusk was gathering when, at the height of Dempsey's worries about the cook, Old Alec came into the office. Without a how-d'y-do, he stood his snowshoes in the corner, unharnessed his pack, and got on immediately with a ritual that never varied when he arrived at a camp. Pulling a chair up close to the stove, he sat with his elbows on his knees, cupped his face in his hands, and allowed the bald top of his head to bake for perhaps half an hour. Then, taking a comb from his hip pocket, he gravely combed his white spade beard for maybe fifteen minutes more.

When Dempsey and the scaler came in, he hardly gave them notice. We went to supper, and afterwards Percy Dawson, Sandy MacDonald and Phil Leonard joined us in the office. The talk was desultory. I could see with what anxiety Dempsey awaited Old Alec's judgment on his table.

If he said, perhaps, "That's a hell of a cook y' got there, Dempsey," then Dempsey and everyone else would know that Alec had enjoyed his supper, and that our worries, after all, might be groundless. If he said nothing at all, there would be real cause for concern. But Old Alec did worse than that; he praised the cook.

"Dempsey," he said, "ye've got th' best danged cook there south of Fifty-nine." That night Dempsey and Dawson decided to go to the City.

Their object was to locate Joe Lavoie, by reputation and performance one of the finest camp cooks in the Minnesota woods. Rumor, probably accurate in this case, had it that Joe was on a bender of considerable proportions in the City.

Dempsey's and Dawson's plan, as they worked it out in the office that night, was a simple one. First they would locate Joe. They would reduce him to a state of unconsciousness—a condition toward which he had, no doubt, already made good progress. They would then bring him to the camp, conceal him until sober, fire the cook, and install Joe in his place.

The initial step was to see Mrs. Burns. Mrs. Burns had

a boarding house in the City where lumberjacks, seeking something bigger-time than the Point in Mokoman, often put up when they "came down" in the spring.

Mrs. Burns was plump and blonde, and she wore moccasins and a big white apron sprinkled over with red dots. She had a little parlor with white curtains, a horsehair lounge, and a pink conch shell on the golden oak center table. The lumberjacks who hadn't any homes to go to seemed to like sitting around in Mrs. Burns' parlor, smoking their pipes and not saying much.

When the camps broke, and when the drives came down later in the summer, many of the men turned over some of their pay to Mrs. Burns. She would allow them enough for a respectable spree and would return the remainder when they were sober again. While a man was still liquored up, no amount of pleading could induce Mrs. Burns to loosen her hold on his roll.

When Dempsey and Dawson called on Mrs. Burns, they found that she had part of Joe's bank roll, sure enough, and she had received more or less regular reports on the progress of his campaign against the City's liquor stocks. She was able, in fact, to name the specific saloon in which, at the moment, he was most likely to be found. For Dempsey and Dawson, the rest was elementary.

Joe Lavoie was an indoor-looking man, white of skin and thin of hair, and he had a soft air and appearance about him that was deceptive. On the second day after taking over at Dempsey's, he asserted his authority in the cook-shanty by throwing out Axel Gustafson, who had thoughtlessly come to breakfast in his undershirt.

93

CHAPTER NINE

I

*E*ACH MORNING at four o'clock Jake Jebault, the shanty-boss, took a chew of Climax, snapped his galluses, and roused Dempsey's crew for another day of logging.

Over in the cook-shanty the lights went on at about the same time. The cookees bestirred themselves among their pots and pans, while the cook himself went sleepily about the business of breakfast for the men.

It was the first task of the shanty-boss to turn out the teamsters, a duty he performed somewhat gingerly; for experience had taught him no sure way to predict the reactions of a two-horse-skinner on being informed that daylight had at last arrived in the swamp. He might (it was most unlikely) smile drowsily and thank you for calling him. Much more probably, he might wake up fighting; or, worse, he might even fetch you an unexpected kick with a hard and bony foot. Jake, you would have observed, trailed a canthook handle as he made his rounds.

The teamsters, up and awake at last, pulled on their socks and boots and groped their ways to the barn, where by the light of lanterns filled and polished by the barn-boss, they fed, cleaned and harnessed their horses. Back to the bunkhouse then, where they splashed a little water on their faces, neatly combed their hair, and sat themselves on the deacon seat. It was now time for Jake to blow the "gabrel."

You could tell a good deal about a camp from the way the crew was turned out in the morning. In some, for example, the shanty-boss simply yanked open the bunk-house door, yelled, "ro-o-l-l-l out!" at the top of his rude and raucous voice, with a few highly personal references, perhaps, tossed in for good measure; and you could be sure that was not a very happy camp. Or, at the opposite extreme, were camps like Scotty Boyle's on the Embarrass. "Give 'em Larry," Scotty would say to a young Irishman on his crew, and the men would be apprised of the beginning of a new day by the sweet, tenor strains of "Larry O'Sullivan." But that, the majority of loggers would agree, carried a good thing a bit too far.

Most well-regulated camps took a middle course and relied on the firm, yet inoffensive, notes of the "gabrel" to get the men out of their bunks.

The "gabrel," a slender tin horn from five to eight feet long, was used not only to awaken the crew, but to call the men to breakfast and supper as well; and in the hands of your average shanty-boss, it was merely a means to those ends. But not so with Jake Jebault. When Jake placed the mouthpiece under his handlebar mustache, pointed the "gabrel" at the Big Dipper, and gave out—that, as all who had ever heard would attest, was something the Archangel himself might have listened to with professional admiration.

For Jake was unique, perhaps, among all "gabrel"

blowers; he had taken lessons on the instrument. He had studied the "gabrel" with a veteran bugler of the war—a bugler by the name of Stiles, the one, it was said, who had sounded the charge on San Juan Hill. And Jake's remarkable renditions might, indeed, have been his own interpretation of that famous call—plus a few phrases, perhaps, from "Yankee Doodle Boy," and possibly a touch or two of moose calling. In the deep stillness of a winter morning, with the stars shining cold and clear in a sky of midnight blue, Jake's "gabrel" seemed to possess a singularly sweet and liquid quality. It was a fine thing to hear its silvery notes rolling and echoing through the pines, or coming to you, wild and beautiful, through the roar of a winter gale; it was a fine thing to hear, even at half past four o'clock of a bitter cold mid-December morning.

Whether or not the rest of Dempsey's crew shared this feeling, I do not know; but they all responded promptly, nevertheless. Breakfast was served at five o'clock, and it waited for no man. So swampers, sawyers, and skidders began to pop out of the bunkhouse, to do as nature urged in the frosty darkness; and to fill the cold, thin air with the sound of sharp reports, as they relieved themselves of the flatulence brought on by heavy meals and a diet over-rich in proteins.

Promptly again at five Jake blew for breakfast, and a stream of hungry loggers flowed from the bunkhouse to the cook-shanty door, a slow leisurely stream if the weather was fine, a hurrying agitated one if the cold bit sharply. And Dempsey would be there when the first of them arrived. Dempsey took nothing, not even a cup of tea, for breakfast; but he never failed to occupy his place at the head of the table, as became the boss.

Breakfast over, the teamsters, landing men and loaders departed immediately for their stations in the woods, while the remainder of the crew returned to the bunkhouse, there to await orders. Presently Dempsey, having conferred briefly with his straw-boss, would stomp into the camp.

"Well, boys, let's try it again!" in Pat Dempsey's bull-like voice. And sometimes, for added emphasis: "Keep things handy around here, now!"

It would still be dark, and the men would walk to work in the darkness, usually arriving just as the first pale daylight began to sift through the pines. Sometimes they built fires and waited for light by which to log. And sometimes they began loading the big hauling sleighs by the light of lanterns made from vinegar jugs filled with kerosene and fitted with candle wicks, and hung from trees.

II

Shortly after we moved to Dempsey's camp it became necessary to "cut" the hogs we had driven over from Tobin. The operation was long overdue. The animals had grown almost to full size, and were half-wild besides, so the task was no pleasant one. It fell to the Olson brothers, two large, fresh-faced farm boys from Pine Falls.

Their equipment for the job was of the simplest: a sizeable case knife in a leather sheath, which they honed industriously to a razor edge, and a bag of coarse salt.

97

Their procedure was equally simple and direct. Selecting a boar, both boys dived at it in the manner of a football player making a flying tackle, while the rest of the hogs milled madly about in squealing panic. A brief, violent struggle in the snow—a few quick passes of the knife—a handful of salt cast into the wound—a thumping kick, for good measure, as the shrieking, pain-mad animal scrambled to its feet. Then to the next victim among those huddled in stupid, silent fear in the farthest corner of the pen.

This went on for the best part of the day. It covered the Olson brothers with gore and gave them a tremendous appetite for supper.

III

In the evenings, Dempsey and his straw-boss, Percy Dawson, would sit by the stove and plan their logging operation. Often it was a stormy collaboration. They would argue and shout, and grow almost violent at times; yet it was rather like a general and his staff planning a campaign, I thought. In so many ways, they had the same factors with which to deal: factors of time, terrain, and economy of means.

Not that there was anything at all theoretical about this business. You could state it in concrete terms, and very briefly. Dempsey's job was to cut the most timber in the shortest time with the least number of men and horses: that is to say, at the lowest cost and greatest profit for the Zenith Lumber Company. Dempsey's success would be measured by just one yardstick: log scale. His reputation rested solely on results. And of this he was constantly, and sometimes gloomily, aware.

Everything depended, in the end, on roads.

The skill with which you ran your roads determined the number of teams and teamsters you would need, the length of your hauls, the size of your loads, and the time you would have to spend in building, icing and maintaining the roads themselves. Nothing save the weather was more important than roads. And so, well up to the middle of December, they were the topic of much of Dempsey's and Dawson's talk and contention, as they pored over crude, hand-drawn maps beside the office stove.

When Dempsey and Dawson first arrived at Tobin late in October, they carried with them cruisers' memoranda on the amount and quality of timber on each of the forty acres to be logged that winter. The objective was to cut this timber and take it to Loon Lake, whence it could be floated in the spring down the Little Sioux, Ojibway and St. Pierre Rivers to Mokoman. The problem: to find the shortest practicable routes between the timber and the landing on Loon Lake.

Dempsey and Dawson had already occupied themselves with this problem for some time when I arrived at Tobin, and by the first of November most of the main routes had been blazed. From then until well after Christmas a good deal of the crew's time was devoted to road building.

Our main hauling road may be likened to the principal stream of a river system. It closely followed Wolf Creek, which insured a down grade over its entire length, and extended from the lake to the back end of the "works"—that is, to the most remote stand of timber. Its over-all length was about five miles. Although the road itself was only ten feet wide, it was necessary in building it to cut a swath thirty feet in width through the timber. When iced to a depth of a foot or more, it formed a smooth crystal highway over which huge loads of logs, sixteen feet wide and ten high, could be hauled with ease by a team of horses.

Into this broad and beautiful highway numerous branch roads fed from the timber like streams into a river. They too were hauling roads, but narrower and iced more lightly, since some of them, perhaps, would be used for only a single day. And, finally, into the branch roads, from the snowy depths of the forest, trickled the narrow skidding trails over which logs were "snaked" by horses to the roadsides. Four "road monkeys" and two sprinkling men were charged with the care and icing of all these roads.

The building of the roads, once the way was cleared of trees, required not only much pick-and-shovel work, but considerable dynamiting as well. There must be no rocks in the roadway; and all grades must be level, or gently descending. So important was this latter stipulation that main hauling roads would sometimes go half a mile "out of the way" to avoid a five or ten foot rise. So, with the aid of dynamite, small cuts were made when necessary; depressions and ravines were filled with dirt and with tamarack, birch and poplar poles. When it was utterly impossible to avoid a steep hill, a "road monkey" was stationed at all times to keep hay or sand in the sleigh tracks.

On the subject of roads particularly, Dempsey and Dawson failed to see eye to eye. Dawson believed in cuts and fills; Dempsey would readily add a quarter to the length of his main hauling roads in order to get a down grade.

"With th' dynamite ye've used on that road, Percy," I would hear Dempsey complain, "ye could fight th' Spanish war all over again."

And from Dawson, doggedly, "Mark my word, Paddy, th' short haul will pay th' best."

Night after night the endless debate lulled me to sleep.

IV

"And will ye ask Jennie if she's got a jar of that honey t' spare, maybe," Dempsey said casually.

He was sending me over to Tobin's for some skidding tongs we had overlooked in moving, and the afterthought about the honey was tossed to me as I climbed into the jumper. Or was it an afterthought? Dempsey was very fond of that honey—it was of a peculiar sugary sort that tasted very good on Mrs. Keeler's hot bread—and he had consumed great quantities of it while we were eating at Tobin.

I wondered about it as I drove along through a Norway pine wood behind Dempsey's gray, and I decided that it was for the honey, actually, rather than the skidding tongs, that I was on the road to Tobin's. Either way, I was content to be going. It was luxury to be traveling in the jumper, a low, two-runner sled with a box behind the driver's seat—so much better than trudging afoot along the snowy track.

It was a serenely quiet morning in the pine wood. The sun came up and flamed against the eastern side of every tree in bright vermilion; the wavy shadows were cobalt blue across the snow. There was no life in the wood, except for a flurry now and then of snowflakes—those wintery little birds so like their names. Nor was there any sound—save the restless stir, of course, that always moves through the forest, even on the stillest of days. On the other side of the wood somewhere I could hear the sawing crews at work—the clang of their saws, faintly, and occasionally shouts and the crash of a tree falling.

It was delightful to glide along in the jumper; but the cold began to get to me after a while and, securing the reins, I ran along in the rut behind the sled, flailing my arms and working my knees high to whip up the circulation of my blood. I was not sorry when we came into sight of Tobin's camp, at last, and the smoke curling up from Mrs. Keeler's big camp range.

Jennie was almost embarrassingly happy to see me, and Cherry, too, seemed pleased. They were sitting beside the stove when I came in, Jennie sewing a patch on one of Big Bill's shirts, and Cherry looking through a Sears, Roebuck catalog. Big Bill had boarded off the kitchen end of the cook-shanty, and the big room, together with the adjoining cook's quarters, made a snug and pleasant apartment. It smelled, as always, of coffee and newly baked bread.

"Mercy me!" Mrs. Keeler exclaimed, taking off her spectacles, the better to see me. "You must be nearly froze —drivin' all that ways. It's real *cold* out today."

She hastened to pour hot coffee for me, to set out thick slices of fresh bread—with some of the honey that Dempsey craved so powerfully—and to press cookies, doughnuts, and more coffee upon me. Then, happily watching me eat, she asked for the news—the news about Dempsey's camp, Mokoman, myself. And I, grateful for the comforts she had provided, gave her whatever scraps of gossip I could muster.

Dempsey was having trouble with soft ice at the landing, and I told her all about that. I mentioned the barrels of turkeys we had ordered for Christmas; commented on the high wages we were having to pay—$40 for teamsters, $35 for swampers; described the close call that Johnny Powers had when a "widow maker" almost got him. Thus, I brought her up to date on the happenings at Dempsey.

And I gave her the news about Mokoman also: there was talk of the new Soo Line extension coming that way; fires were breaking out all over town, because of the severe cold; and, with the stock running wild about the streets, a cow had got into old Mrs. Cooper's storm shed one night and had frightened her half to death—she was going to sue the city.

Cherry didn't listen much to what I was saying—or appeared not to. She went through the catalog in the preoccupied sort of way, turning the pages she had read and re-read, I knew, many times before. I watched her as she paused over the parasols, the books, the electric belts, the graphophones, the hats, the hair rats and switches. I wondered what her brooding thoughts were that morning as her eyes wandered absently over the petticoats, the violins, the stereoscopes.

Mrs. Keeler sighed.

"I'd like to get down once this winter," she said, "just for a couple days, maybe. I'd like to go to early Mass on Christmas." She looked a little guilty. "I ain't been to Mass since I made my Easter duty."

She sat silently for a little while, a strange, dreamy, pleasant look on her plain face. Her eyes, back of her gold-rimmed spectacles, I noticed for the first time, were dark and intense, like Cherry's. But softer.

"It's been awful lonely here since you all moved away. Sometimes I think I jest can't stand it any more—not ever seein' anybody. I get such a cravin' for somebody to talk to. Cherry don't talk much, and Will don't neither."

Mrs. Keeler mused over the cup of coffee she had poured for herself.

"It's like the cravin' I get for greens," she said. "Seems, sometimes, like I can't wait till spring t' get a mess. . . . Dandelions is awful good. Back in Michigan I used to dig some for my Ma, real early in the spring, before the blossoms come. You can make a salad of 'em, with bacon drippin's and salt and pepper, or you can cook 'em and eat 'em with vinegar. . . . Pigweeds is good too. Lots of people don't think so, but they're good too, if you pick 'em real young. . . . Course, beets is best. I wish I had a good mess of 'em to go with th' boiled pork tonight. . . ."

"I could go for some myself," I said heartily. But I said it only to be sociable; I had no fondness for greens.

"Do you know something?" Mrs. Keeler asked, her eyes brightening. "Do you know what I been thinkin'? I bet there's greens out there right now—under all that snow. It's *warm* under the snow. I bet there's green things down there, maybe dandelions, or wild mustard—that's good too, with vinegar, same's you fix dandelions, or pigweeds. . . . If you dug down in that snow, I bet maybe you'd find some. . . . Wish I could get Will to try. . . ."

She sighed again, but more in resignation than sadness, and began to clear the table. As she moved about, she began to sing a little song. It was an odd sort of tune, in a low, minor key, and it consisted of only a few notes repeated monotonously. The words were even stranger than the air:

> The bell must toll,
> The bell must toll,
> God help me now
> To save my soul.

I sat in a sort of daze, trying to make some sense out of Mrs. Keeler's talk about digging down into the snow for greens, and listening to her lugubrious little song. She sang it over and over and over. Suddenly Cherry, with what might have been a sob, jumped up and rushed from the room.

V

As I drove homeward, with the jumper box full of tongs and with a jar of sugared honey for Dempsey, I carried with me a feeling of depression and sadness. I sat hunched up on the seat, seeing none of the lovely winter sunset, and not noticing until we were almost upon it the small figure trudging along in our track ahead. I pulled up the gray and shouted to give warning of our approach.

As we drew nearer, the figure, which was clothed in a sort of hooded *capote* made of red blanket material, stood off the road and turned to face us. At first I thought the dark, small face in the hood was that of a boy. Then I saw it was a girl's face, oval and delicately modeled, and with the small high cheek bones, the dark eyes and blue-black hair that, in our country, always hinted of Indian blood. I glanced down and saw that she wore moccasins, beaded in the Chippewa fashion.

"Going my way?" I asked. "We're from Dempsey's camp."

The girl smiled in her frosty hood.

"Thanks," she said in the soft, gentle voice that Indian women often have. "I'm cutting across the lake." She waved a mittened hand in the direction she intended to go.

I wanted to say something else, but could think of nothing appropriate; the gray, impatient to get back to the barn, was tugging at the reins. So I let him go, and we left her rather abruptly.

I looked back through the swirl of snow the gray kicked up and saw her still standing at the edge of the road, looking after us. I waved to her and she waved back.

CHAPTER TEN

I

*I*T WAS lunch time in the cook-shanty, and the barn-boss, as was his mid-morning and mid-afternoon custom, was pouring tea. He poured himself another quart or so and reached for his fourth slice of coffee cake.

"All this here goddam sweet stuff," he said, waving his dollop of cake, "there ain't no *good* in it. Ain't worth a hoot 'n hell—'cept t' burn a feller's stummick out."

"Tell us about th' time you was whackin' bulls on th' Saginaw," said one of the cookees. "Tell us about them days again, Butch."

The barn-boss chose to ignore any overtone of sarcasm in the cookee's invitation.

"In them days, Joe," he said with dignity to the cook, "in them days men et like men. A feller'd come in from his work. He'd take his goddam plate an' cup. He'd go over t' th' fire, an' th' boss'd dish up his grub fer him. He'd git his beans and bread and tea—an' maybe some pork—an' he'd take his goddam plate over t' th' deacon seat an' he'd sit down an' eat his supper."

The cook absently pushed the pan of coffee cake toward the barn-boss, who absently helped himself to his fifth slice.

"No sir, no mess of sweet stuff," he said, "t' ruin a man's guts in them days. Beans every day—an' potatoes once a week, maybe, t' keep away th' scurvy."

He surveyed the "mess of sweet stuff" spread out on the table before him: fine white breads, baking powder biscuits, raised doughnuts, crullers, buns, rolls, fruit cake, cookies, coffee cake, pies. His face expressed disdain, but his hand presently reached for a doughnut.

"An' we done th' work," he added, "we done th' work of six of these here lizzie-boys calls theirselves loggers 'round here."

You could hardly dispute the barn-boss's main thesis: that Dempsey gave his crew breads and pastries in large amounts and great variety. All logging camps of that particular period did. Some said the canny operators had discovered that it was cheaper to fill a crew up with sweet breads and jelly cake than with beefsteak and fresh pork. But it would be fairer, perhaps, to say that such lavishness was merely typical of the open-handed way in which most camps set their tables.

"How's the grub?" Invariably this was the first inquiry a new man made about a camp. Good loggers followed a good table, and on that basis camp foremen bid for them; Dempsey had always been a high bidder.

When the men filed into Dempsey's cook-house and silently seated themselves at the long, high, oilcloth-covered tables, they sat down to the best the woods could offer.

II

In the covered space between the bunkhouse and the cook-shanty—the "dingle"—the meat was kept. From the cross beams hung quarters of beef, frozen as hard as red Minnesota granite. Here, too, were suspended the scrubbed carcasses of hogs, each split in twain as though with a single stroke of a giant cleaver. And here were barrels of corned beef (and cabbages to go with it), boxes of smoky sausages, barrels of marble-white salt pork, sacks of brittle Lake Superior white fish. And even barrels of turkeys awaiting Christmas!

To all of these good materials Joe Lavoie gave the respectful attention of an expert cook. At his two big steel ranges he prepared the roasts, the steaks and Irish stews which fortified the men three times a day. Without fail, we had beefsteak or sausages for breakfast; a roast or stew, and often both, for supper; and beans, of course, for every meal. The cookees—discreet men!—passed continuously up and down the long tables, eyeing the deep tin dishes, making sure that none was ever empty.

In the roothouse, a musty hole dug into the hill side and shored up neatly with spruce poles, the smell of the earth merged with that of potatoes, rutabagas, turnips and carrots. These, with the inevitable navy bean and an occasional mess of sauerkraut, were all in the way of vegetables that we were ever to know at Dempsey's. Leafy foods never appeared on our tables; and, had they been available, it is doubtful if there existed the camp cook with the courage to serve them. Yet, if any of our crew suffered from a vitamin deficiency, he was not aware of it.

Canned fruits were, at a later date, to appear for the delectation of other logging crews, but the only variety we knew at Dempsey's was the dried kind. We had prunes, sometimes referred to with rather strained facetiousness as "loggin' berries," apricots, apples and raisins. These Joe Lavoie dished up as stewed fruit, in puddings and in pies—especially in pies, which he turned out in vast quantities. In addition, he made "Larrigan" or "shoe-pack" pie, also referred to by a completely unmentionable name, from cornstarch and vinegar; and lemon pie from lemon extract, a flavoring ingredient which was highly regarded in the camps, as well, for its drinking qualities.

Except for a few minor variations, such as steak and flapjacks for breakfast, and tea for lunch, our menus differed little from day to day, or from meal to meal. On any day, we might have expected such fare as this—and much the same on every day thereafter:

BREAKFAST

Oatmeal, with condensed milk and sugar
Pancakes, with syrup and oleomargarine
Beans, baked
Beefsteak or sausages
Fried potatoes
A variety of breads, coffee cake, etc.
Tea and coffee

LUNCH

Roast beef
Beans, baked
Mashed potatoes
Mashed rutabagas
Coffee cake, doughnuts, bread
Pie
Tea

SUPPER

Roast beef, hot or cold
Cold boiled pork
Fried potatoes
Beans, baked
Cabbage
Bread, buns, etc.
Pie, cake, cookies
Tea or coffee

At noon the "lunch horse" brought us our food in a boxed-in jumper, stowed in large tin cans which we placed near the fire. Sometimes the sled which carried the lunch to the men in the woods was called a "swing-dingle," but at Dempsey's camp, horse and sled were referred to collectively as the "lunch horse," just as tote-sleigh and horses were known simply as the "tote-team." Thus, a man might say, " 'Bout time th' lunch horse showed up, ain't it?"

We ate our mid-day meal sitting on a skidway log or the bunk of a hauling sleigh, striving with cold-stiffened mouths to eat our beans before they froze to the tin plates.

The old-timers cut a few balsam boughs and placed them on the snow beneath their feet; it helped to keep them warm. The horses, blanketed against the cold, had their noon ration of oats.

At breakfast and supper we went rather formal. We did not, for example, thoughtlessly come into the cook-shanty wearing our hats, or without our shirts—two breaches of etiquette which the cook was likely to consider a personal affront, and react to accordingly.

Nor did we take any place at the table except the one assigned to us on our first day in camp. The rules of precedence were as strict at Dempsey's as at a diplomatic dinner. Each day the men sat in their proper places on the long benches, their galluses forming a row of large white X's against their colored shirts: at the head of the first table, Dempsey; at his right hand and left, the straw-bosses; then each man, according to his proper station, down to the lowly swampers.

III

And, so, as we came into the cook-shanty for our supper, we found ourselves in a long log structure, very similar in construction to the bunkhouse, except that it is caulked on the inside with swamp moss. At the far end of the room, as we entered, we saw the cook's battery of two steel ranges, their ovens opening toward us; next to them his work table; and near-by two barrels of hot water, heated by coils from the stoves and handy to the sink. The back door opened on Wolf Creek; a door at the left gave entrance to the store room.

Here Joe Lavoie, immaculate in white shirt and apron, prepared his succulent roasts and stews, cooked his vegetables in shiny tin steamers, fried his flapjacks by the hundreds on large, rectangular griddles, and baked his beans in a heavy cast-iron pot with a lid that must have weighed twenty pounds.

He was assisted in all this by the cookees who, wearing colored cotton shirts and white aprons, also peeled the vegetables, set and cleared the tables, and washed the dishes, shaking them with a terrific din in flour sacks to dry them. The bull-cook, wearing whatever he was lucky enough to possess, kept the ranges supplied with 16-inch tamarack firewood and saw to it that the water barrels were kept well-filled from the creek.

At a long board against the right hand wall, beneath a central window and flanked by shelves for dishes and cooking utensils, Joe turned out his limitless flow of breads and pastries, cakes and pies. Their sweet, fresh fragrance filled the cook-shanty as we entered.

The four long oilcloth-covered tables were set with steaming food; and at each man's place was his deep tin plate, upside down, and on top of it his handleless tin cup, also bottom up. The cookees stood in solemn white-aproned silence at the head of each table. We silently seated ourselves.

And in silence—or, at least, without conversation—we ate our supper. There was no small talk during meals: this was one of the most rigid rules of the woods. No one knew exactly why, but it was a rule everywhere observed. Some say it was a peace precaution, designed to eliminate arguments, and hence fights. Others think it was enforced for the cook's benefit, to speed up eating and clear the tables quickly. If the latter, it was a successful regulation, for it was a rare meal at Dempsey's camp that lasted longer than ten minutes.

Only at the mid-morning and mid-afternoon snacks, when the barn-boss, the handy-man, the scaler or a straw-boss dropped in for a cup of coffee, was there leisure and conversation at the table. Only then did Joe Lavoie allow himself a few minutes of relaxation from his job of preparing two hundred and fifty meals a day for hungry loggers. Listening to the barn-boss grow nostalgic about the old days on the Saginaw, he was skeptical. He merely smiled, however, and allowed the scaler to speak for him.

"Maybe you et like men in them days, Butch," the scaler remarked, "but how many of youse is left to tell about it?"

IV

The handy-man jammed himself abruptly through the office door, banging it shut against the crackling cold outside.

"Boss," he announced, "the Big Sister, she's here."

Dempsey hoisted himself out of his bunk where he had been enjoying a Sunday afternoon siesta. The long raw-hide laces of his boots trailed after him as he shuffled toward the window.

114

"Th' Little Sister, she's wid her," said the handy-man. "They do be havin' a shot of coffee in th' cook-shanty."

Dempsey, trying vainly to see through the frosted window, worried a chew of tobacco from his plug of Spearhead.

"Why don't they give a man some warnin'?" he asked plaintively. Then sudden indignation appeared to seize him. "Why in th' hell don't they let a feller know?" he bellowed.

He subsided immediately, however, groaned and returned gloomily to his corner, a defeated man and well aware of it.

"Clerk," he said bitterly, "we're bunkin' with the crew tonight. Will ye kindly inform the shanty-boss of th' same?"

"They came in wid th' tote-team," the handy-man volunteered. "I t'ink th' liddle one's got her snozzle froze."

Dempsey grunted and spat experimentally from a prone position at the sand box under the stove. It was a long and difficult shot; he missed it. The handy-man scuttled through the door again.

Each winter, in their black Benedictine robes, they visited the camps—the Big Sister and the Little Sister. Their names were Sister Catherine and Sister Angela, but few knew that; everybody just called them the Big Sister and the Little Sister. They visited the camps each winter, making the rigorous circuit in the cutters and jumpers of various camp foremen. Come blizzards, come cold, come weather that drove the very logging crews inside, the Sisters were certain to arrive. You could count on them—

the way you could count on the walking-boss, or Dangling Dailey, or Roothouse Pete. Sooner or later during the winter, wherever you might be on the St. Pierre or Ojibway, the Big Sister would find you out and sell you a hospital ticket.

And, for all the grumbling of bosses, clerks and scalers, ousted for a night or two from their sleeping quarters, the Sisters were not unwelcome guests in any camp. They were old-timers, and the old-timers everywhere knew them for one of themselves. They brought you the news and gossip from town, from the other camps, from the world "outside"—news and gossip about mutual friends and acquaintances. They could tell you where old Tom Bassett was, and whether Pa Porter was drinking again, and how many feet of timber Jerry Frazer expected to land on the Snake this winter, and maybe they'd seen your wife and kids, if you happened to be a married man.

They were *real* old-timers. Paddy Hogan could remember the first time he had seen the Big Sister in the camps, and that was all of eighteen years before. The Little Sister was with her then, Paddy said, folding her hands in her big sleeves the same, and hardly ever speaking. And the Big Sister hadn't changed much either; a little heavier, maybe. But her face was fresh and pink from the weather then, the same as now, her eyes blue and frosty, and her big voice booming out, as it always would, no doubt. . . . We could hear it now as we came into the cook-house, Dempsey and I, to greet her.

"Joe," she was saying to the cook, "they were telling me at Terry Lynch's that you're getting married."

"*Oui*," he beamed. " 'Bout time Joe Lavoie he's got heemself a woman—some little wans—eh?"

"Yes, about time, Joe. That's what I've been telling you the past ten years."

"*Oui,* 'bout time," Joe agreed.

"And when is the wedding?" the Big Sister asked.

"Oh, I don' know—nex' spring—nex' summer, maybe," Joe said vaguely.

The nuns laughed, the Big Sister heartily, the Little Sister like a gentle echo. When we came in, they turned to shake hands with us. Dempsey greeted them with grave courtesy and a great, and no doubt genuine, show of hospitality. For some time they chatted, like the old and good friends they were; then the Big Sister said: "You have a fine set of camps here, Pat."

"Aye," Dempsey agreed. "We do be livin' in style this winter."

"And the best cook in the woods," she said, with a nod toward Joe.

"We-e-ll—we've lost none of th' crew yet."

Joe Lavoie roared with appreciative laughter while Dempsey, amused and a little lofty, turned to serious talk with the Big Sister.

"They do be tellin' me Ed Gleason's contractin' on th' Bug."

"And losing his shirt," the Big Sister said.

Their conversation drifted off to distant camps and long gone days, and it lasted until almost supper time. After supper Dempsey called the men's camp to attention and announced the Sisters' presence.

Many of the men came into the office during the evening to buy hospital tickets. Old Dunc MacLean, as usual, was not among them. Old Dunc sat obdurately on the deacon seat in the bunkhouse and would have none of either the Sisters or their tickets. Once, when in a weak moment he had allowed himself to be taken to St. Stephen's Hospital, an indignity had been perpetrated upon him which he never forgave: they had made him use a bedpan.

In the morning Dempsey had the gray hitched to his jumper and he himself drove the Big Sister and the Little Sister to Hank Horan's camp on the Ojibway, reflecting with satisfaction, no doubt, that they would arrive late in the afternoon—and without warning.

V

"Ever see any Indians around here?" I asked Les Crosby.

Ever since I had seen the girl in the red *capote* on the road to Tobin's. I had been wondering about her. Who was she? Where was she from? What was she doing in these woods?

Except for Mrs. Keeler and Cherry, she was the first woman I had seen in two months, and quite naturally, perhaps, her face kept recurring to my memory. But it was a dim, faint image of a face, for I had caught only a quick glimpse of it in the frost-rimmed hood of the *capote*.

"Ever see any?" I again asked of Les, who was slow to answer a direct question.

He had come in for tobacco, and I thought that from

118

him, if from anybody, I might learn something. For, although Les was a teamster, he had for many years been a trapper; he knew each quarter section of this region as I knew the streets and corners of Mokoman. By some accident in the woods, he had lost one eye, but the other was bright and blue as a baby's in his weathered face. With this good eye Les now regarded me, I thought, a little sourly.

"Don't see nawthin' much but horses' rears nowadays," said the ex-trapper. "But I *usta* see Indians in 'round here all right.

"Blackjacks and La Prairies—they used t' camp over on Beaver," he said, referring to a large lake that lay south and west of Dempsey. "Whole families of 'em—bucks, squaws, papooses, dawgs—knew 'em all in them days." He paused reflectively. "Don't know as many's left no more."

I could see, in his one good eye, a reminiscence coming.

"Mind th' time years ago," he said, "when I made their camp just 'bout dark of a miser'ble cold day. Th' snow'd covered th' water hole, so I pokes my head into one of th' wigwams and inquires if anybody there c'n help me find it. They was lots of people in there, includin' a mess of kids, layin' 'round with their feet to th' fire, and Joe Blackjack—th' lodge was his'n—says somethin' in Chippewa, and a couple of th' kids jumps up and runs out on th' lake t' find th' water hole fer me.

"They ain't got enough clothes on t' flag a hand car, but that don't bother *them* none. They finds th' water hole fer me, and then they plays tag out there on th' lake fer awhile—runnin' 'round like a couple squirrels in their bare feet and nothin' but their thin little shirts and pants t' keep out th' miser'ble cold, by God.

"Most of them Blackjacks is gone now," Les said. "Old Joe Blackjack and all th' rest of 'em. Gover'ment moved 'em down to th' reservation—put 'em in houses. Indians don't last long in houses, gener'lly."

Les hadn't yet answered my question, but in the next sentence he did even better.

"Tell y' what we might do, clerk," he said. "One of these days you and me might wheel over and see if any of them Indians is still campin' on Beaver."

CHAPTER ELEVEN

I

*I*T WAS a fine but sorrowful sight to see the sawing crews bring down the great pines that had been so long growing to their height—the somber white pines and the proud red Norways: they sighed in their lofty crowns as they waited for the undercutter to mark them for death, for the mice-like men to destroy them with saws and felling-wedges.

Comes the undercutter with his beautiful, double-bitted ax. His calculating eye runs to the upper branches of a century-old pine; he notes its lean, its field of clearance; he checks the wind's direction. Then, at precisely the proper point, his ax sinks into the rough, clean, cork-like bark.

The undercutter's strokes have a deadly, professional accuracy; the kerf left by his blade is as smooth as paint; the chips that fly out upon the snow are as large as a man's hand, and cleanly curved. The pine is quickly and deeply notched *on the side toward which it is to fall,* and the undercutter, pausing for a chew of tobacco, gives over to the sawyers.

The big crosscut saw, six feet long, goes to work on the opposite side of the trunk, at a point several inches above the lowest part of the undercut. It *clangs* rhythmically as the mittened hands of the sawyers draw it back and forth. At each pull of the saw the teeth bite through half a dozen annual rings—half a dozen years of growing. At each pull long "ribbons" of sawdust are ripped from the trunk.

Presently the great band of steel is buried in the tree; when it is completely out of sight, the sawyers drive steel wedges into the kerf. One of them takes from his hip pocket a whiskey flask encased in sheet metal; it contains kerosene which the sawyer pours on the saw to dissolve the pitch, the oozing life-blood of the pine. They resume their sawing, and at the end of each long, steady stroke their breath rises in a little white cloud on the frosty air.

Zang—zang—zang—the saw bites relentlessly through thirty years of growth . . . fifty years . . . seventy. . . . The heart ring, the original seedling-wood that grew, more than a hundred years ago, in this once silent forest, has long been severed; the end is near.

Suddenly comes the warning *cr-r-ack!*—sharp and crisp, like the report of a rifle. A few more strokes of the saw, and then a rending, tearing sound: the death rattle of the great tree. "Timber-r-r-r!" The traditional cry, half in warning, half in triumph, rings thinly through the woods; and the sawyers, looking to their footing, step away from danger, while all in the direction of the tree's fall scurry for safety.

The pine, however, does not come down at once: it hesitates, trembles, seems to resist the wordless indignity it is about to suffer. But the mice-like men, the tiny blades and even tinier teeth of steel have wrought irrevocably. Slowly, very slowly at first, the great trunk begins to totter, to lean a little in the direction that the undercutter, with the first stroke of his ax, determined it should fall. Then faster, as fibers snap and rend. The branches moan their protest as they sweep downward through the high air; the moan grows now to a whistle—to a shriek—as the big green-top gathers speed.

The crash, of course, is tremendous, as the great pine comes to earth in clouds of snow and showers of broken twigs and branches. But the litter settles down, the branches of the fallen tree wave up and down for a little while, from the impact of the fall; then everything is still again, and the swamper comes to do his work.

He "tops" the fallen pine, lops off the great branches with clean, expert blows of his ax, and throws the brush onto a pile, out of the way of the other workers. The resinous scent of the mutilated tree fills the wintry air. And how *long* it looks, stretched out in the snow! So much longer, even, than when it stood upright and living among its fellow pines.

It will make four logs below the first branches, this tree, and the undercutter marks them off, putting the bark mark on each one. White pine logs are made from twelve to twenty feet in length, with sixteen feet the standard; Norway pine logs may vary from twelve to thirty-six or even thirty-eight feet. No other species of tree is cut at Camp Dempsey, save a few spruce and tamarack; no birch nor poplar. Some loggers, including Dempsey, are superstitious about the latter; they refuse to work in a camp that cuts "popple."

So, our pine is down, dismembered by the swamper, bucked into sections by the sawyers, and hauled ignominiously away by the skidder. And thus, day after day, our six sawing crews at Dempsey's turn the ancient forest into a wreckage as ugly as the devastation of fire, hurricane or war.

Usually we made two, and sometimes three, separate cuttings—like a barber "going over" a customer several times, leaving the poor and "punky" trees till last. This lessened the danger of trees breaking on those already down. The work of the sawyers was facilitated, and the brush was less bothersome. No "green-tops" were ever left —good pine, difficult to skid to the hauling roads, were cut down and left to lie, so that the standing tree would not catch the eye of the walking boss.

Always we started cutting from the rear end of the branch roads, so as to keep the hauling ruts free of bark. And, as I think I have already mentioned, we left the timber around our camps until last.

During the winter of 1906 we put in a total of 6,127,476 feet of white and Norway pine: enough, the barn-boss averred, to build a fancy-house with 50,000 rooms.

II

One bright night, along toward Christmas, Roothouse Pete came into camp. He arrived as quietly and unobtrusively as one of the shadows of the rising moon, found himself a corner in the bunkhouse, and immediately after breakfast on the following morning disappeared into the roothouse.

Nobody knew anything about Roothouse Pete except Dempsey, who knew his name. Nobody knew anything about him at all save that, in whatever camp you happened to be, Roothouse Pete was certain to show up during the winter.

His eyes may have been blue, or gray or hazel, but they looked black, they were so deeply sunken in his pale, small face; and they were about all you remembered of Roothouse.

Nobody knew what language he spoke, because he never talked. When he came into a camp, he did not ask for employment. He did not report at the office; he simply went into the roothouse and started sorting the vegetables there. He culled out the spotted carrots and rutabagas and turnips, and he sprouted the potatoes. When he had finished the job at Camp Dempsey, he drifted into the office and stood silently at the counter, and I knew he had come for his time. I made it out, and Roothouse Pete went on to Terry Lynch's camp.

Throughout the winters Roothouse Pete made his way from camp to camp, disappearing like a burrowing mole into their damp, dark roothouses, sorting their vegetables, until he had come to have a sort of fungus look and smell about him. All the camp foremen had known him for many years; and, although none ever hired him, none ever refused to pay him for the work he did.

When I try to recall Roothouse now, after nearly forty

years, I see only those large, wild eyes, and what I remember as their darkness may have been only what lay behind them.

III

"Will ye take a look at that?" said the Whiteface Liar. He tossed a small, hard object to Noonan, the cross-haul teamster.

Noonan caught the object and examined it closely. It was hard and nugget-like in appearance, and had a grayish metallic luster.

"What's it look like, Noonan?" urged the Liar.

"Looks like a hunk of lead," said Noonan.

"Lead me eye!" the Liar said. " 'Tis silver. But little I'd expect ye to tell th' difference, of course."

Noonan scratched the object experimentally with his thumbnail.

" 'Tis silver, sure enough—pure silver," said the Liar. "And"—he paused impressively and lowered his voice—"somewheres—up on th' border—they is a whole island of silver where that come from. A island of pure silver."

Noonan looked up, startled.

"I been on it," said the Whiteface Liar.

He looked about him guardedly.

"I'd just as lief, Noonan," he said, "ye'd keep what I'm goin' t' tell ye to yerself. I'd just as lief ye didn't let this go no further.

"What I'm relatin' happened back in '87—maybe '86, I fergit exactly which. Time me an' Jonas Ireland (God

126

rest his pore soul!) was nosin' around up north of Vermilion.

"Jonas an' me'd just bought a new birch bark canoe off'n a Indian. . . ."

The Liar paused and considered.

"Well, maybe we didn't exactly *buy* that canoe." He amended his statement. "We offered t' buy it, I mind, but th' Indian didn't want t' do business. So that night Jonas an' me come back an' took possession, which we figgered we had th' right t' do, havin' offered t' pay fer it, an' it wasn't no fault of our'n if th' Indian didn't want t' do business.

"Well, anyhow, we pushed along purty hard that night an' got into some lakes I didn't know th' name of. Don't know if nobody knew th' name of them lakes—don't know if they *had* no name. But some of them was purty good size, an' Jonas an' me went prospectin' 'round fer two, three days without even seein' another Indian. Then, one evenin', we come t' this here island."

The Liar held out his hand for the nugget, which Noonan dropped into it.

"We come t' this island," he resumed, "small island— maybe quarter mile long—wooded with spruce. Looked like any other island. No difference. 'Count of th' mosquitos bein' bad, Jonas an' me decided to make camp on it. So we paddles over an' pulls up our canoe.

"After supper we set fer awhile by th' fire, smokin' an' watchin' th' pike jump in th' lake, an' Jonas is pokin' around under th' moose moss with a stick, th' way a feller does, an' he loosens this here little rock, an' it rolls my way.

"I picks it up, intendin' t' toss it out'n th' lake. Then I notices how heavy it is. Passes through my mind: 'Curious a little rock like this bein' so heavy.' I looks at it—jest th' way you been lookin' at it, Noonan. Scratched it with my fingernail, jest like you did. Then I gets excited.

" 'Take a look at this, will ye, Jonas?' I said, not darin' to tell him what I was thinkin'.

"Jonas looked—same as you did. 'By God, Whiteface,' he says, 'by God, I believe 'tis silver!'

"I don't have t' tell ye, Noonan, we was both purty excited by this time. We started scrabblin' around, pullin' up moose moss, collectin' rocks and scrapin' at th' black coverin' with our knives.

"We run up an' down that island—pickin' up small stones, gougin' at big boulders. Every rock we scratched shined like a new dollar. Every place we scraped away th' dirt—pure silver. Everywhere th' same—pure silver. *We was on a silver island!*"

"Christ almighty!" said Noonan, before he could stop himself.

The Liar smiled—sadly, it seemed.

"As ye might surmise, Noonan," he said, "Jonas an' me danged near burned th' bottom out'n that Indian's canoe, gettin' down to th' City.

"We took th' samples to a assay office. Ninety-six percent pure silver.

" 'Where'd ye get these here samples?' th' feller in th' assay office says t' us.

" 'Wouldn't ye like to know?' we says t' him.

"Next day we was headin' back with a surveyor—old friend of Jonas'—t' locate th' island, so's we could homestead it."

Suddenly the Whiteface Liar seemed to wilt. The excitement and the enthusiasm went out of his narrative. He gazed at Noonan dejectedly.

"Noonan," he asked, "ye have been in th' border lakes?"

"Some of 'em," Noonan answered.

"Well, then, ye know how they is. And ye know about th' islands—millions of 'em—and all lookin' alike."

"I know well," Noonan said. "I mind th' time I was lost in th' islands on Big Sag fer three days—"

"Then ye will not laugh at me, Noonan, when I tell ye this. Fer eight days we searched th' lakes above Vermilion. Fer eight days we wint from island t' island—ontil our grub run out. . . ."

The Liar gazed sorrowfully at the small metallic object in the palm of his hand.

"Some day, Noonan," he said in a sort of whisper, "I'm goin' back an' find that silver island."

IV

We had two "jumping Frenchmen" at Camp Dempsey: Jo-jo Poquette and little Louie Le Fleur. I do not know what nervous affliction caused them to "jump," but it seems to have been one that affected only French-Canadians. It was a source of great amusement to some of the crew, and of distress to Jo-jo and Louie.

If you would come up behind Jo-jo when he was talking to someone and suddenly shout, "Hit him!" Jo-jo would strike out at the person with whom he had been speaking. Once, when he was working on the river, Jo-jo had jumped off a boom into the water when a fellow riverman had yelled "Jump!"

Hank Feeley, Joe Gachot and a few of the others took delight in tormenting Jo-jo and Louie in this manner. Little Louie was even more fun than Jo-jo: he not only jumped; he sometimes cried.

V

Those who happened to step into the office while the job was being done were naturally curious. They wondered why Dempsey was having a trap-door cut into the floor. But the handy-man met all inquiries with his usual owlish blink; and I, having been instructed to keep mum, gave out no information.

"Dangdest fool thing I ever heerd of," said the barn-boss indignantly. "Trap door goin to nowheres!"

The answer to the mystery was not, however, very spectacular after all. That very night the tote-team drew up to the office door and a barrel was unloaded. Dempsey, with great deliberation—the door having been locked—pried the head out of the barrel, and at once the cabin was flooded with the round, delicious fragrance of—apples. Ohio Baldwins, they were—the bloom still frosty-blue on their deep red skins. Fancier varieties of apples have since been developed; and, as with the Pippin and the Jonathan, you meet but seldom with the Baldwin nowadays. But show me the fruit that can compare for sturdy character and robust, wintry goodness, with those noble apples which we sampled, smiling at one another with appreciation, around the office stove that memorable evening.

Carefully we lowered the treasure beneath the floor and closed the trap door over it. Dempsey had planned wisely. In no other way, certainly, could his little store of apples have been protected against almost instant demolition by the crew; by no other means husbanded through the winter, like bottles of rare wine to be brought up occasionally for the enjoyment of the boss and his friends.

For me, however, Dempsey's apples were also a source of trouble.

Every lumber camp had its malingerers—men who "laid in" on pretense of some illness or other and worked just enough to warrant feeding them. One of ours was Joe Gachot.

Gachot took to spending a good deal of time in the office, not because he imagined that I enjoyed his company, but, I am sure, for precisely the opposite reason. And he studied ways to irritate me. He would help himself to a pair of socks, or cut himself a plug of tobacco, writing the record of his purchase in the account book himself. Then, pawing through the book, he would discover some entry of a purchase which, he protested, he could not recall. Although he never charged me directly with falsification of his account, he managed by insinuation to annoy and anger me, which was obviously his aim.

Particularly, because he had observed that I took no pleasure in hearing them, he delighted in long and nauseating recitals of his experiences in brothels, and of his beastly adventures in the Philippines campaign. Even at this distance of time, I feel the same sickness in the stomach that I felt then, when I heard Gachot's thick voice recounting his sordid escapades.

Sickening and repulsive Gachot often was, and sometimes vaguely sinister, but never openly belligerent. On the contrary, he occasionally put on a smirking show of friendliness which, in a way he no doubt considered subtle, concealed the grudge he bore me. Under cover of this manner he angled for one of Dempsey's apples.

"Seems t' me I smell apples somewheres," he said, sniffing affably. And, when I said nothing, "How 'bout it, kid? Let's sample 'em."

"They're the push's apples," I said, without looking up from my work. "You'll have to ask him."

"Th' push don't care," Gachot answered carelessly. "He said fer me t' help myself."

He shuffled over to the trap door. He stood and contemplated it for a while, looked at me with a sly grin, then stooped as if to pull it up. Before he could hook his finger into the little countersunk ring, however, I sprang from behind the counter and took my stand on the door.

"Maybe he did," I said, "but he told me not to let anybody in there."

Gachot straightened up; he had a malevolent grin on his reddened face.

"Look, clerk," he said softly, "you wouldn't refuse a guy jus' one little apple, would ya?"

"They're not mine. They're Dempsey's."

Gachot seized me by the arms and playfully attempted to shove me aside.

"Cut it out, Joe," I warned him. I was tense and nervous. "I'm not fooling."

Nor was Gachot . . . any longer. His face, already red, grew apoplectic, and a little scar on his forehead came out suddenly, as if someone had quickly drawn it there with a white pencil. And, as I looked at his angry features, I knew where I had seen him before.

"Okay, kid," he said thickly, "ya can shove your goddamned apples. Gimme a plug of Spearhead."

I cut a section off the slab and handed it to him across the counter. He looked at me squint-eyed as I did so.

"Say," he asked slowly, "ain't you th' guy that spilled my booze that time in Mac's place?"

"I guess maybe I am," I answered.

"I-I-I *thought* so!" Gachot said. He grinned unpleasantly and reached behind him for the door handle. "Well —like I said—I'll be seein' ya!"

CHAPTER TWELVE

I

*J*ESUS*!* I just give him a chew of tobacco," the horse-skinner whispered.

He was almost as pale as little Jo-jo Poquette, lying there on the snow with his head crushed in.

"Couple steps more and he'd a-made it," one of the swampers said. He said it almost hopefully, as if there were still a chance of Jo-jo's escaping death.

Along with the rest of us, the swamper had watched Jo-jo make his run for it. He had started in plenty of time, all right; but the wind caught the big top on its way down and had swung it out of its true course. Jo-jo must have sensed the danger over his shoulder, because, without looking back, he suddenly veered to his right and scrambled frantically through the drifts.

But he was a small man, and the deep snow hampered him. As the pine swept downward, Jo-jo moved in a straight line toward a point beyond its path. It was a sort of horrible mathematical problem working itself out: a problem involving two objects moving in intersecting planes. And the answer to the problem was life for Jo-jo Poquette, or very sudden death.

For a moment or two it looked as though it were to be

134

life; then Jo-jo bogged down in a drift, for an instant only, but long enough to erase his slender chance of escape. While we whooped and yelled frantically, the great pine completed its shrieking arc of death, and Jo-jo was lost to our sight in a crash of tossing branches and clouds of flying snow.

"Couple more steps would a-done it," the swamper repeated, as if that could be helpful now.

The horse-skinner exhibited the plug of tobacco from which Jo-jo had taken his last chew; it still showed the marks of the dead man's teeth.

"Just now give him a chew off'n this plug," he said. "He's still got it in his jaw there."

"For Christ's sake, shut up," Sandy MacDonald said. He brought Jo-jo's feet closer together and stood up. "Jake, run back to camp and get the jumper, will you?"

Jake, the road monkey, started hastily on his way and the rest of the men stood uneasily about, looking at Jo-jo with a sort of curious unbelief. Some of them felt a little guilty, I guess—the ones who had taken so much delight in tormenting the small "jumping Frenchman." And all of them were shaken by what had happened.

Not that sudden death in the woods was a novelty to them. The hazards of logging were many indeed, and it was a lucky crew that got safely through the winter without some serious mishap. Most loggers took a certain pride in this fact. For they were all a little vain of living dangerously as well as hard, and around the bunkhouse fires "narrow escapes" were, next to women, perhaps the most common topic of lumberjack talk. Few lacked a rousing tale or two to tell.

Death often came swiftly and in unexpected forms. Your ax might glance and cut an artery and, in a temperature sixty degrees below freezing, with no one handy with the slightest first-aid skill, you could be almost certain that your time had come to "take a walk." A tree caught in a high wind or deflected from its course by another tree might get you, as one had got Jo-jo Poquette. It could jump sideways from its stump, or in spite of the cunning mechanics of the undercut, "kick back" with all the violence of a steam-driven piledriver. There were many ways a murdered tree could take its vengeance.

If you were a hauling teamster, there was always the danger of your load "breaking" on a hill and hurtling dozens of sawlogs upon you and your helpless horses.

Were you a top-loader, that most perilous of all occupations in the woods, there were a hundred ways in which you might be crushed or knocked from your load as the logs came bowling up the skids. Or you might be killed, as many were, simply by the falling of a branch that had been hanging in some tree.

Death of the sudden, violent sort was not uncommon in the woods, but it jolted the men, nevertheless, when it occurred—as was plain enough when you looked at the tense faces and listened to the nervous talk of those who had seen little Jo-jo "get his." They were uneasy and restless until the jumper came and took him away; and one of the skidway men went behind a pile of slashings and was sick.

They passed the hat for Jo-jo, as was customary with loggers, and collected nearly a hundred dollars. It was all his widow would get to bury him with. There were no workmen's compensation laws in 1906; and the companies, which grabbed all and gave nothing, had scant interest in a corpse that could neither swing an ax nor jump a claim.

That night they put Jo-jo in the feed shed, where he froze very stiff, and the next morning he went down to Mokoman with the tote-team. Louis Le Fleur, his friend, accompanied him.

II

December 15th

Yesterday's big snowfall is piled up everywhere and the plow is out with six horses again, trying to clear the main roads. Dempsey is discouraged. The men spend half their time in the woods, he says, shoveling snow. But worse, the ice refuses to freeze solid on the lake, and perhaps won't until February. Temperature this morning was just under zero.

December 17th

It is very cold, 32 below zero this morning, but so clear and dry that the frost doesn't stick to the men's whiskers. It is excellent logging weather, with plenty of snow to grease the skidways.

This afternoon I saw a flock of snowflakes running here and there near the feed shed. It was about the biggest flock I have ever seen, almost a hundred of the little birds, I would guess. As I watched them feeding cheerily in a windswept spot, keeping up a tinkling little chirp all the time, I thought of my mother. She has a special place in her heart for these wintry little birds, and always puts out some of the chicken's feed in our backyard for them. She says you can be sure that winter has really arrived when the snowbirds begin to visit you.

December 20th

Jerry Miles, who has somewhat of a reputation as a "boomer" anyhow, decided today to go down and "set" in the mills on the winter run. Dempsey got wind of it and asked me to have Jerry's time all made out and ready for him. So when Jerry came into the office after supper to announce, rather shamefacedly, that he was quitting, Dempsey immediately hauled the time check out of his pocket and handed it to him. "Gee, you keep things handy around here!" exclaimed the astonished Jerry. Dempsey considers this a great joke and repeats it to everyone.

Lately I have spent more time than I should, I suppose, thinking about the Indian girl I met on the road to Tobin's camp. I wonder more and more *who* she is, and *where* she is from.

December 25th

Christmas! The one day of the year except Sundays when nobody—save the cook, cookees, bull-cook, barnboss, shanty-boss, sprinklers *and* camp clerk—do any work. It has been a beautiful, suddenly warm day—and we had *turkey* for dinner. Joe fixed it up with stuffing, cranberries, mince pie and a lot of extras—just like he used to do it at the Ritz, he said. It certainly was enjoyed by all as much as anything ever served at that famous hotel.

Quite a few of the men received packages with food and Christmas gifts in them. A Waterman fountain pen, with the patented clip cap, is my gift from Mother and Carlie, and a most welcome one! I am sad to think of them having Christmas alone this year—the first without my father and me.

Somehow or other a little whiskey had been smuggled into the camp to celebrate the Yuletide with, and there was a good bit of singing in the bunkhouse, the first I have heard in the woods. But instead of Christmas carols, they sang "The Little Brown Bulls" and "The Jam at Gerry's Rocks." Louis Le Fleur, Joe Lemieux and Johnny Chapados sang some French-Canadian songs and afterwards the crew had a "stag" dance.

Lights are out in the bunkhouse now, and Dempsey appears quite relieved that we have got through the holiday without trouble. Someone in the City sent him a very Christmasy-looking necktie which he, in turn, presented to the bull-cook with great formality and many expressions of good will.

II

Crosshaul Carlson, some claimed, could speak with horses; and perhaps he could, for the old man had been associating with them for half a century or more, and he certainly did things with a skidding team that no other horse-skinner, or hair-pounder, at Dempsey's could approach.

Others, however, said this was merely a matter of Crosshaul's bribing his animals with chewing tobacco. A great lover of Climax plug, Crosshaul customarily gave his horses a chew (it was said) whenever he took one himself; and, while this ran up his tobacco bills scandalously, it won for him a most remarkable degree of co-operation from his nags.

Crosshaul's horses avoided hidden obstacles with uncanny prescience as they snaked a sawlog through the woods; they maneuvered it upon the briding almost without guidance; and, on occasion, they had been observed to glance back over their shoulders to see how things were coming along!

But most skidding horses, for that matter, were uncommonly intelligent animals—which, as many a woods boss had wryly pointed out, was more than could be said for most skidders. With their driver and an individual of generally limited capabilities called the "chainer," two skidding horses formed not the least important half of a basic logging team known as a skidding crew.

At Dempsey's we had six such skidding crews. When the great pines had been felled and sawn into logs, it was the job of these crews to get the logs out of the deep woods to the skidways, where they could be loaded onto the hauling sleighs and taken to the landing. For this essentially simple operation there were several techniques.

Usually a pair of tongs resembling ice tongs was used. These tongs, when firmly "set" in the small end of a log by the chainer, would tighten as pull was exerted and would grasp the log firmly while it was being dragged over the snow-covered ground to the skidway.

For larger logs and longer hauls, however, the skidding crew resorted to the go-devil. This was nothing more than a stout, prosaic-looking sled consisting of hand-hewn runners connected by a heavy crosspiece, or "bunk." Upon this bunk one end of the log was rested, while the other dragged upon the ground.

And thus, with difficulty when the ground was soft, with ease when it was frozen and "greased" with snow, the skidding crews snaked their logs through the woods and tangled slashings to the skidways. After the ancient way of all drivers of draft animals, they facilitated their work with a little profanity. But the average horse-skinner, it was averred by those who had heard both, was but a pale reflection of the awesome bull-whackers who, not so many years before, had done the job with epic invective and oxen.

When Crosshaul had lugged a sawlog to the skidway, it was "decked" for the loading crew; that is to say, it was pulled over a small ramp, called a "briding," onto a pair of medium sized logs laid about eight feet apart at right angles to the hauling road.

This was the skidway proper, and here Louis Paul Joseph, a swarthy, over-sized French-Canadian, performed with tremendous enthusiasm and élan the job of skidway man. The canthook in Louis' gigantic hands was a ridicu-

141

lously puny toy. He would slap it upon a big sawlog and, with a heave of his shoulders and a joyous shout, send it rolling down the skidway like a beer bottle down a bar. And so, with many a whoop and *sacre bleu!* Louis Paul Joseph packed together from fifty to seventy-five logs, with perhaps a few on top for extra measure, side by side on his skidway. Throughout the hauling season there was a continuous flow of logs from these skidways to the hauling sleighs.

Louis Paul Joseph, as skidway man, had another duty which he performed with great enthusiasm—that of stamping the logs with the Company's stamp mark. This he accomplished by leaping from log to log and striking each end with a long-handled stamp ax, which left the Company's mark in the wood. These stamp marks, serving exactly the same purpose as cattle brands on the ranges, were usually changed from time to time; but the Zenith Lumber Company had kept its mark, the letter Z in a square, for many years.

Some of the well-known marks of lumber companies in the Mokoman area were:

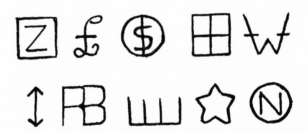

There was only one Louis Paul Joseph at Dempsey's camp, but there were six skidways in all, and six skidding crews to keep them decked up, and six sawing crews to provide the logs. The skidding crews and the skidway men worked manfully to get ahead of the sawing crews, to "get them up a tree." There was no greater disgrace for a sawyer than to have a skidding crew run out of logs to skid; for a skidding crew, there was no greater triumph.

IV

"How 'bout that there trip over to Beaver?"

Les Crosby asked the question while inspecting a pair of horsehide teamster's mittens.

"Sure," I said quickly. "How about Sunday?"

It had been almost a week since our talk of the possible Indian village on the lake, and I was increasingly curious to see it—if, in fact, such a village still existed. Or, perhaps I should confess that I wanted very much to see the girl in the red *capote* again.

The vague image of the small face in the rimy hood continued to haunt my memory. I had glimpsed it so briefly that I recalled it only imperfectly and, as the days passed, this quality of vagueness merged into one of mystery. There was a certain strangeness, too, in the girl's very presence on the lonely Tobin road—any girl's; I came to feel a sort of unlikeliness about my ever having met with her at all. And so, more and more, my imagination was intrigued; she was often in my mind.

"What do you say?" I asked Les. "Sunday?"

"Yep," he said. "Put these down ag'in me, clerk." He held up the mittens. "I got a fish house over to Cedar," he added. "You and me might stop on th' way over fer a try at th' pike."

The rusty winter dawn was just showing above the ridge when, on the following Sunday, we struck off through the pines for Cedar Lake, which lay in a direct line, south-west, with Beaver. We traveled light, carrying only our lunch, a small hand ax, and a five-pronged spear head that the blacksmith had made for Les. In about an hour an old portage trail brought us to Cedar Lake, a mile-long oval of dazzling white, walled all around by a heavy stand of pine. The snow on the surface of this lake was criss-crossed by the tracks of innumerable wolves; it was so hard-packed that, creaking and squealing, it bore our weight as securely as ice.

At the far end of the lake a black cuneiform object stood out in the blinding whiteness like a swimming spot before our eyes. This was Les' fish house, a rude framework of poplar poles covered with tar paper.

The wind at that end of the lake had swept the snow somewhat thinner and Les, after a little scraping around, located the spot where he had formerly cut through the ice. Although the lake had frozen to a depth of at least a foot, the ice was only four or five inches thick in the hole; we soon had it chopped out and the opening cleared. The water under the ice looked as black and opaque as onyx.

Then occurred a startling transformation. Les and I pushed the little tar paper house over the hole we had cut. Immediately the dark, lusterless water was flooded with a wonderful brilliance—as though a thousand electric bulbs had suddenly been lighted in its depths.

I looked down for many feet, it seemed to me, into the clear, green translucence, streaked with moving veins of stronger light and crossed occasionally by fleeting, phosphorescent shadows. Crouched in the small, light-tight house, I gazed in fascination while Les, outside, cut a shaft for his spear. I fully expected a curious fish or two to make an appearance; and, sure enough, one did. A great pike, as long and thick as my arm, with a flat shovel nose, swam lazily into my field of vision, as though into an underwater spot light, flipped his tail and disappeared beneath the ice.

His spear properly rigged, Les prepared to fish. From his mackinaw pocket he took a small wooden minnow, weighted with lead, gaily painted and equipped with shiny tin fins. This he lowered into the water on a line. With his left hand he jerked the line up and down; the lure darted about, very life-like and enticing in the bright, mottled water, as Les crouched, spear poised in his right hand, over the hole.

I waited expectantly for my fish to return. Les patiently bobbed the lure up and down, up and down; it darted busily about, a temptation, one would have thought, to any hungry pike. But none, alas, showed any interest. The cold began to seep through my heavy clothes. We were out of the wind in our little house, but we were cramped and immobile, too; my trousers began to feel chilled and metallic against my legs, my toes and fingers to ache with the frost.

Finally Les had a strike. A good-sized pike lunged at the minnow, apparently changed his mind in the lightning interval of the strike, and merely batted the lure aside. At the same instant Les jabbed furiously with his spear; he missed, muttered something into his frosted mackinaw collar and resumed his patient bobbing. Presently, another strike—another miss. The cold was attacking fiercely now. I began to grow concerned about the chances of being seriously frost-bitten; but Les, who must have been quite as cold as I, continued patiently and intently to bob over his hole.

Suddenly his seemingly endless patience was exhausted. Without comment, he reeled in his minnow and wound the dripping line around it. "Le's git over to Beaver," he said.

Beaver Lake proved to be much larger than Cedar, and it was dotted with rocky islands wooded with spruce and balsam. It lay below us—for the trail dropped suddenly downwards from where we stood—crisp, precise and immaculate, like a damask table cloth strewn with bits of jade. Les squinted at the lake with a searching woodsman's eye.

"See anythin' over there?" he asked, pointing across the frozen bay to which, it was apparent, our trail would lead.

I looked closely along the far shore, where a birch forest came down to the water's edge. It seemed to me that I could discern a cabin or two settled in the drifts.

"That's them," Les said. "That's them all right, but don't look like nobody's around."

We decided, however, to investigate. When we neared the shore we could make out a few cabins, low and crude and all but buried in the wind-heaped snow, together with the forlorn skeletons of half a dozen teepees. As we came still closer, several dogs—battle-scarred, ragged-eared curs—dashed at us viciously. A cabin door opened, and a man came out swinging a steel trap at the end of a chain. He drove off the dogs with many shouts and menacing gestures.

"*Bo-jo, nitchee,*" Les said to the man, in the familiar Chippewa greeting: "Hello, friend."

"*Bo-jo,*" the man responded gruffly.

He was a very dirty and unpleasant-looking Indian, and our visit appeared to give him no pleasure. Les tried to converse with him in stumbling Chippewa. He seemed, for the most part, to be asking questions, for the Indian repeatedly grunted, "*Kawin,*" a word which I recognized as "no."

Now and again our friend absently swung at one of the dogs with his trap. While he and Les were talking, I studied the little huddle of cabins in the background. All except one—the one out of which the Indian had come—appeared to be uninhabited. This one had a small glazed window and through it I tried hard to see into the interior of the cabin. Once I imagined I saw someone moving about inside, and I held my breath—fearful, I realized, that it might be the girl of the red *capote.*

"*Bo-jo nin-dan negeeway,*" the Indian said abruptly. He took a final swipe at the dogs and turned his back on us.

"What did he say?" I asked.

"He said, 'Good-by, I'm going home,' " Les laughed.

As we headed back across the bay ice, Les told me what he had got out of the Indian; it wasn't much. Nobody lived in the settlement any more—expect for a little while in the spring of the year, during the sugaring-off season, and again in August when the wild rice, which grew in the small lakes thereabouts, was harvested. Our informant was at present trapping. Everyone else had been moved down to the reservation. . . .

"But who—" I started to ask.

"Who what?" Les said.

"Nothing."

I plodded along in the trail behind Les, pondering my private mystery, and hesitating to ask the direct question which might, quite possibly, have cleared it up at once. I was over-chary, perhaps, of being guyed; but there was also a certain fascination in trying to work the puzzle out in my own way.

Dusk was gathering in the pines when we reached Cedar Lake again, and Les, instead of cutting across the ice, followed a route along the shore.

"Don't never get caught out on th' ice 'round dark where they's wolves," he said.

We arrived back at Dempsey's, tired, hungry, and too late for supper—and I no wiser than before about the girl I had met on the Tobin road.

CHAPTER THIRTEEN

I

CHERRY came over from Tobin early one afternoon, and tossed an envelope on my counter.

"Pa wants this to go down with Ed in the morning," she said.

She took off her mackinaw and hung it on the corner post of Dempsey's bunk; shook some snow drops from her hair. She was flushed and bright-eyed from her walk.

"It's a letter Pa wrote to his brother, Harley," she explained. "Pa only writes to Harley about once a year. But when he does, he can't wait for the letter to get there."

She sat down on the edge of the bunk and reached her hands out toward the stove. She was wearing a strong perfume that immediately pervaded the room.

"I was glad of the chance to come over and gab with someone," she said.

She paused, looked at me contemplatively, and made a moue.

"I don't suppose that's mutual though," she added.

Before I could say anything, she asked softly, "What's the matter with you, anyhow? Don't you like girls?"

I could never find a proper answer for Cherry's sudden, discomfiting questions.

"Oh, sure," I said lamely. "Sure, I like *some* girls."

"But not married ones. Is that it?"

Cherry laughed and threw herself back on the bunk. "Well, don't worry, Matt. I won't bother you." She gazed at the planking of the upper bunk and went on, "Not that you don't bother me—sometimes."

"Speaking of girls," I said, over-loudly, "I met one on the Tobin road that time I came over for the skidding tongs."

Cherry sat up quickly.

"You *did?*"

"Yes—about a mile from camp. She had on a red coat with a sort of hood. She had dark hair and dark eyes, and—"

"My! You remember everything, don't you?"

"Well, that's about all," I said self-consciously. For the sake of saying something, I added: "I thought maybe she was an Indian."

Cherry burst into sudden laughter.

"What's so funny?" I demanded.

"I was just thinking," Cherry said. "You mixed up with a squaw."

And that's all I could get out of her. I had hoped for more. But if Cherry knew anything about the girl in the red *capote,* she had decided to keep it to herself. She lay back on the bunk again. Our conversation became more and more desultory, and before long Cherry was asleep.

I turned to my camp books and tried to forget her, purring gently there in Dempsey's bunk. But that, as the afternoon wore on, became increasingly difficult; and I grew more uneasy. I was apprehensive of someone coming into the office and finding Cherry there. When the handy man, on his way to the barn, paused as if to drop in, I held my breath. I decided I must waken her.

Cherry was napping soundly. Her lashes were dark and shadowy on her sleep-flushed cheeks, and her breath came in little purrs—like a kitten's—through her parted lips. As I looked down at her, with her dark hair unloosened against the gray of Dempsey's blankets, I knew why I disliked her.

It was because I was afraid of her. I was afraid of her even while she was asleep. And my arm shook as I reached out to awaken her.

I had to shake her hard to get her up, and when she came fully awake, at last, she was petulant. She took a cigarette from a small pasteboard box of "tailor-mades," lighted it, and looked around at the sloping shadows in the room. Her cigarette was chalk white in the soft raspberry red of her mouth. I remember this strange detail because it was the first time I had ever seen a cigarette between a woman's lips.

Cherry looked at me sleepily through the up-curling smoke.

"Why didn't you wake me sooner?" she demanded.

"I thought you were tired, and it's a long hike back to Tobin," I said, as casually as I could manage. "Maybe you'd better get started."

Cherry studied her cigarette (which she held a little awkwardly) and shrugged.

"Don't rush me," she said. "I've got lots of time. I'm a fast walker."

But she remained no longer than it took her to finish the cigarette. At the door, on her way out, she turned and drawled:

"So long, Matt. You can relax now."

Joe Gachot, as luck would have it, was the first of the crew to come in after she had left. He looked around, sniffed curiously, and remarked, "Smells like a canhouse in here."

When I had passed his box of snuff across the counter, he looked at me with something like a leer and said:

"Saw Cherry Gordon down the road a ways."

He didn't say any more than that, but continued to look at me with a knowing grin. When he had gone, I brought some green pine boughs in and burned them in the stove, with the lid off, to get rid of the smell of Cherry's perfume.

II

If some dark night, on one of Dempsey's lonely logging roads, you should have met with a huge and monstrous shape which, as it came slowly toward you, belched clouds of smoke and steam, and from flaring torches cast wild, magic-lantern shadows on the agitated pines—that, of course, would have been the Galloping Twins out with the sprinkler.

The Galloping Twins were not twins at all, actually, but brothers only, Bert and William Ross by name. Still, they were like enough, at that, in stature and flaming hair and beards, for twinship. They were large and bashful men who spoke their few needful words with a gentle lisp, and it was their business to keep our roads iced for the hauling sleighs.

Rigorous work it was, too, with all the icing done at night, and the temperature well below zero for weeks at a time. But the Twins carried on cheerfully enough, quite unmindful, it seemed, of the terrible cold—except that sometimes before going out they would come into the office and ask for a little turpentine ("turps" they called it) to smear on their faces for protection against freezing.

Their sprinkler was a great wooden tank about twelve feet long, mounted on iron-shod runners and holding 3,000 gallons of water. It was filled from a hole cut through the ice of a small lake near our main hauling road.

So that the water in the sprinkler would not freeze, an old boiler had been placed inside the tank, and in this boiler was built a fire. For light to show them their way over the dark forest roads, the Twins attached two torches on long poles just aft the driver's seat. And so, equipped against both cold and darkness, they would set out with their frosty horses to ice our roads in the black and bitter hours when all the rest of us at Dempsey's slept.

As soon as solid freezing weather had set in—which was about the middle of December—the Galloping Twins were out with our sprinkler every night. And within a week our main hauling road was paved with a smooth sheet of crystal about six inches thick and strong enough to carry a full sleigh-load of logs. During the winter this

153

pavement was built up, by repeated icings, to a thickness of ten to twelve inches, and was usable until early April. Long after all the snow had vanished, save in the deep swamps, our highways of ice, standing perhaps half a foot above the barren ground, still wound their way through the forest. Our secondary roads, having received only a light icing, broke up much earlier.

When the Galloping Twins were not out with the sprinkler, they likely enough were going over the roads with the bull-rutter. This was a sort of combination snow-plow and rut-cutter; for deep grooves, or ruts, had to be cut into the ice, to receive the runners of the sleighs and keep them securely to the road. The bull-rutter required a crew of three—a teamster, and two men to control the sharp steel cutting knives.

The Galloping Twins were quietly proud of their custody of the bull-rutter. When, once a week, and usually of a Sunday morning, their sharp-shod horses pulled the great machine—like some ancient engine of war—grinding and scraping, with the peculiar sound of metal cutting into ice, over the hauling roads, then an expression of almost embarrassed contentment suffused their big red faces. For the job of cutting ruts that were true and sharp, tracks in which the great sleighs would glide smoothly and steadily, without "shimmy" or wobble under their tremendous loads—that was a job for experts.

Because the Twins did most of their work at night and slept during the morning, they often came over to the office in the afternoon to pass the time of day. Neither of them was very "handy with a pen," and so I sometimes

did a letter for them—usually to their mother in Mokoman—which they would sign jointly in their large, childlike hands, "Your loving sons, Will and Albert."

III

It was Sunday morning at Dempsey's, a bright, white,
proper sort of Sunday morning; and behind the bunkhouse the landing-boss and the Whiteface Liar were
"boiling up."

During the whole length of the winter, of course, baths
were foregone at Dempsey's camp, but many of the men
fastidiously changed their underwear once a week, a habit
which made it necessary to "boil up," or launder their
clothes each Sunday. For this purpose one large iron
"camp kettle" was provided.

Phil Leonard and the Whiteface Liar had been up
since four o'clock, waiting their turn at this kettle. And
now, at shortly after ten, they had at last come into possession of the communal laundry.

They poked idly with "popple" poles at the contents of
the kettle, which was filled with water they had carried
from the creek and suspended over a small fire for which
they themselves had cut the wood. The Whiteface Liar
fished up a dead gray something that might have been an
undershirt. He tried again and brought to the surface an
object which quite certainly was a sock. This he regarded
critically for a moment, then allowed it to slip back into
the simmering liquid, and resumed his conversation with
the landing-boss.

"Yes, sir, Phil," he said, "that shore was a bad winter. Miser'ble cold it was, if ever I seed it cold. . . . I'm referrin' to the winter I was doing a little spot trappin' up on the Border."

The Liar poked a ballooning pair of drawers well under water.

"Wasn't as bad for me, though," he went on, "as it was fer Old Man Corrigan. The old man had a reg'lar trapline up in that neck of th' woods, and he was bothered some by bears."

The Liar paused, considered, and corrected himself.

"Old Man Corrigan," he said, "was bothered *somethin' fierce* by bears. Seems like every time he put up fer the night in one of his side camps, these here bears would show up. Awful bold they was. Actually'd set round th' fire, kinda lickin' their chops and a-waitin' fer him t' turn in. Then they'd git into his grub and mess things up somethin' terrible."

A swamper sauntered by, looked into the camp kettle and asked, "Don't yuh think yer stew's about cooked, Whiteface?"

"As I was sayin', Phil," he resumed, "the bears gets bolder and bolder, and fin'lly they breaks into the old man's head camp and danged near wrecks everythin' in it —includin' his blankets. Point blankets they was, too, Phil, but I never seed th' like of 'em after them bears gets through with 'em. They was tored to ribbons.

"Well, Old Man Corrigan fin'lly gets danged discouraged and decides to give up trappin' on account of them bears makin' life onbearable fer him."

156

The landing boss added a few sticks of tamarack to the fire. "I s'ppose that's where you come into th' story," he said.

"How did you know, Phil?" the Liar asked in surprise. "That's right. I was pokin' around in the same neck of th' woods short time after that and one evenin' I comes across a old cabin on Jackfish lake. The dirt had sifted down through th' roof poles and they was tracks on th' floor that looked like bears'd been in there.

"They was also some blankets in th' bunk, but they was all tored t' ribbons, and I recognized 'em right away fer Old Man Corrigan's blankets he didn't bother t' take with him on account of th' way they was ripped up by th' bears.

"It was a miser'ble cold night. So I makes up th' bunk and, account of it bein' so miser'ble cold, I piles what's left of Old Man Corrigan's blankets on top of my own, and I hits th' balsam.

"I'm sleepin' sound, with my head down under th' blankets, ontil I'm woke up by th' noise of somethin' movin' around in th' shack. I pokes my head out of th' covers t' see what th' hell's goin' on, and I'll be danged if there ain't two bears standing big as billy-be-damned right in th' middle of th' floor.

"In them days," the Liar explained, "I gener'lly toted my old Peacemaker 'round with me in th' bush—handy fer gettin' game and such. Got so I was purty good with that gun after while. Could cut th' head off'n a partridge half as far's from here t' th' barn. Used t' nip th' tails off'n th' red squirrels fer th' fun of it. Ever been up round

157

Kawnipe? Ever noticed how most of th' squirrels is missing of their tails up there? Well, I camped one summer on Kawnipe, and—"

The Liar turned his attention momentarily to the business of boiling up.

"Where was I?" he inquired.

"You was tellin' about bears," the landing-boss said indifferently.

"So I was," said the Liar. "And there they was, too, standin' bold as be-jesus right in th' middle of th' floor. Fortunate fer me, I had th' Peacemaker hangin' on th' wall handy. I snakes it out of th' holster, and lets fly.

"Bang! Bang! Bang!" said the Liar, pointing his finger and cocking his thumb at the camp kettle. *"Bang! Bang!"* he added after an interval.

"Well," he went on, "it was purty dark in that shack, and I ain't certain if I hit them bears or not, but I danged well scared th' pants off'n 'em. They both does a couple a backward flops and streaks hellbent fer leather, one divin' through th' door and th' other straight through th' wall."

The Whiteface Liar lifted an undershirt from the kettle, wound it around his "popple" pole, and heaved it over a limb of a near-by spruce to freeze.

"Don't know if I hit 'em," he said, "but them bears knowed for sure it wasn't Old Man Corrigan in them blankets."

IV

It must be that dumb animals have some prescience of the nearness of death—how else could you explain the behavior of our hogs when, one quiet morning, we slaughtered them, one and all?

There was a smell of blood on the winter air that day, and all the hogs milled around uneasly in their pen. They squealed and grunted nervously, turning all together and rushing first this way, then that, and slipping about in the snow. But among them there was constantly one hog that would act in a special and particular way.

I saw myself how terror would seize upon that hog— the one the Olson boys, sitting on the high spruce-pole pen with a Winchester rifle—had marked next to die.

He would separate himself from the rest of the herd, this doomed hog—or perhaps it was that the others fled from him and his aura of death—and he would scrabble frantically about, his small eyes filled with nameless fear, rushing along close to the fence, crashing blindly into the corner posts.

Then, quite suddenly, he would become still, standing apart and lonely, it seemed, with his eyes closed and making no sound; and, I could have sworn, trembling in a sort of stricken resignation.

And at that instant Carl Olson would slowly raise his rifle and sight along the blue, octagonal barrel; and the hog, very suddenly, would crash to earth as though he had been hit with an invisible hammer. For it was hard to connect his abrupt, violent downfall with the puny report of the rifle.

Thus, over and over, the shooting of the hogs went on for several days. As soon as one had been killed, it was bled and dressed, and taken to a spot near the creek where it was immersed in scalding water and scraped to gleaming pink-and-whiteness. Then, split in twain, head and all, it was hung in the "dingle" between the cook-shanty and bunkhouse, there to freeze and acquire a gleaming coat of frost.

The lumberjacks at Dempsey's, surveying the great store of sweet, fresh meat, fairly drooled with anticipation of pork chops and sow belly, succulent roasts and savory Irish stews, and cold boiled pork. There was always an air of happy anticipation around a logging camp at slaughtering time.

V

To almost every man who had been in the woods for any length of time some story or other had attached; and this story, circulated from camp to camp, eventually became a sort of tag and label on the man about whom it was told. Many a logger thus found his personality fixed forever in an anecdote.

Mostly, they were slight, sly stories, not labored overmuch in the telling. Such a one was the pleasantry about Paddy Doyle who, while foreman of a camp on the Bug River, left his outfit one fine morning in order to campaign for the office of constable. For two weeks the camp ran itself, and no one heard of or from Paddy. Then, marching back into camp as abruptly as he had left it, he made the sole reference he was ever heard to utter regarding his absence, "Well," Paddy announced stiffly, "I ran ahead of me ticket."

160

Much told was the story of Jerry Danker's delivery of the ox to Rufus Dempsey, father of our own camp foreman. That was in the days, of course, before Jerry had become a boss logger himself. He had been commissioned to fetch the ox up to Dempsey's over the almost impassable road leading to the camp. Much against his own judgment, but at Dempsey's bullish insistence (in many respects the old man seems to have prefigured his son's personal traits), Jerry set out with the ox.

Presently he found himself in the heart of a muskeg swamp, with darkness coming on and the ox mired down, like a mammoth in a Siberian bog. All the poor animal's struggles and all of Jerry's efforts and imprecations only worsened the situation until, as the ox settled deeper and deeper into the mire, it became clear that there was nothing for it but to dispatch the unfortunate beast. This Jerry did. Before proceeding on his way, however, he cut off a short length of the ox's tail, which was about all, save the horns, still above the surface of the swamp.

When, long after sunset, Jerry finally made camp, he flung the bit of ox tail down before the astonished elder Dempsey.

"And what in all hell," inquired the latter, "might *this* be?"

"Thar," replied Jerry, with classic simplicity, "thar is yer goddam ox."

And the particular stretch of muskeg in which the ox was lost, it may be remarked in passing, is to this day known as Jerry's Slew. . . .

In addition to such highly personal anecdotes, many tales were told at the expense of anonymous individuals—such, for example, as the story of the boastful Canuck who, having heard the often-used phrase "like a squirrel on logs," asks, "Wat you call dat leedle animal, go sque-e-e-e?"

"I call that a cow." From a bored logger.

"Well, dat," the Canuck says proudly, "dat's me on logs!"

For the most part, this *genre* of logging camp story was aimed at the "foreigner"—at the French-Canadian, usually, and later at the Swede and Finn. In this respect it was characteristic not only of the camps but of a whole era of American life.

Generally, however, the stories told on the deacon seat, around the bunkhouse stove or the campfire of the drive, poked gentle fun at universal human failings—and especially at the most common of all, perhaps: conceit and stupidity. And in this they reflected not inaccurately the true character of the riverman and the logger who, whatever else they may have been, were seldom loud or thick and had little use for any man who was either.

VI

After the deep cold had set in, late in December, we began toting on the St. Pierre and Ojibway Rivers from Mokoman; and, at the same time, it became possible to reach Panger by way of Wolf Creek, either afoot or with the jumper.

Panger was a flag stop on the D. & K. E., a logging railroad running down from the Iron Range and popularly known as "the Dinkey." It was also the focal point of several roads, one of which, the Corey-Nixon road, ran eastward across most of the county, for more than a hundred miles. A few settlers had established themselves in the vicinity of Panger; otherwise there was nothing there except the desolate reaches of the cutover.

Although Panger was of no use as a supply point, it did offer us round-about telephone connections with Mokoman; and it was for the purpose of making a call to headquarters that I made my first trip to the little settlement. And there I again met the girl in the red *capote*.

The only telephone at Panger was in Joe Panger's little general store, and I was cranking it, trying to get the operator, when my eyes fell upon her moccasins. I recognized the beadwork—or what I had taken for beadwork when I had glimpsed it that afternoon on the Tobin road. But now, to my surprise, I saw that the pattern was worked not in beads, but in a sort of embroidery; and not on moccasins at all, but on little felt boots that turned up slightly at the toes in the style of shoepacks.

The girl had her back to me, talking to Joe Panger over the counter, but there was no mistaking the red blanket-coat either. The hood was down now, and I could see her smooth dark hair, just as I had remembered it, hanging in thick braids inside the *capote*.

My connection with Mokoman was finally completed, and, while I explained the urgency of sending up two pair of McLarin castings with Benson, the girl gaily returned Joe's badinage as he filled her grocery order. I couldn't hear what she said, but her laugh was fresh and hearty, like a child's.

I must surely have betrayed my surprise when our eyes met. For hers was not at all the face that I remembered—or, rather, the face that I had allowed to grow in my imagination. It was not an Indian face. The eyes were not black. They were gray—large and gray—but such a dark, shadowy sort of gray that I might have been excused, I suppose, for having thought them black.

It was the moccasins, no doubt, that had thrown me off —or what I had taken for moccasins. My mind had seized on that detail and, by a sort of crazy logic, had constructed upon it a whole pattern of perfectly consistent but wholly erroneous impressions.

But her hair, at any rate, was smooth and blue-black, as I had remembered; and the cheek bones of her small oval face were a little high; and, while her skin was not dark—not Indian dark—it was warm and rich in color. She had an eager quality in her voice that went with her quick smile and the way her nose crinkled when she laughed.

"Why are you so astonished to see me here?" she asked.

I was easily enough flustered by girls in any case, but this sudden question—or perhaps it was the direct inquiry of those unusual eyes—left me for a moment quite speechless. Then:

"I'm not astonished," I remonstrated lamely. "I just— I only—"

She was busily doing up her purchases in a canvas packsack, knotting the rawhide thongs that held the cover down.

"We live here," she said, glancing at me with what might possibly have been a smile of amusement. "My name's Sari Luomala."

"Mine's Matt Bradley," I told her, glad of something simple and positive to say.

"I know," she said.

Once more, I am afraid, I did not conceal my surprise.

"How do you know?" I asked bluntly.

"My cousin Lyyli," she said. "Lyyli has told me *all* about you—even before I ever saw you. Do you know Lyyli Sarvela?"

"Oh, sure. Is Lyyli your cousin? We went to high school together."

"Yes, Lyyli thinks you are very clever. She used to tell me about the clever things you said in the English classes."

"But, Lyyli," I said, embarrassed, "always got the high grades."

"She has a good memory—all Finns have good memories." Sari slipped one arm through a leather strap attached to the packsack. I helped her with the other. She joggled the sack up and down to settle it on her back. "But you were really the smart one."

She said it so matter-of-factly, smiling all the while, that it was impossible for me to tell whether or not she was making fun of me. I opened the doors and carried out a small can of kerosene that Joe Panger had filled for her from a barrel at the back of the room.

Sari had leaned her skiis against the building, beside

the door. They were long, narrow Finnish skiis, beautifully made and decorated with an intricate design burned in the wood. She began to fasten one of them on. All at once I realized how reluctant I was to see her leave, how much I wanted to say something that would keep her for a while.

"Well, you seem to know all about me," I said awkwardly. "But I don't know anything about you."

Sari looked up and laughed. She fastened on the other ski and straightened up.

"Oh, there isn't much about me," she said. "We live down there a ways." She waved toward the Corey-Nixon road. "I teach school in Mountain Iron, but I'm staying home this half. My father isn't well."

"I'm sorry," I said. "Maybe some time—"

Sari waited for me to finish and when I didn't she held out her mittened hand.

"Good-by," she said. "And thanks for helping me."

I shook her hand without finding the words I wanted to say. Sari picked up her kerosene can and lifted her skiis a little with her feet—first one, then the other.

"I'm awfully glad I've seen you—finally," she said. "Sometime when you're over here again come in for a cup of coffee. We're the second farm across the tracks."

I watched her disappear down the road on her skiis. Just before she rounded the curve into the spruce she turned and waved, as she had done on the Tobin road.

CHAPTER FOURTEEN

I

You have heard the story of the Round River drive, no doubt. And you know how Paul Bunyan, after logging a hundred million feet of timber on the Pyramid Forty, broke his rollways and began driving the winter's cut down the nameless river which ran past his camps. How, after two weeks, the drivers came to a hill that looked vaguely familiar, and a set of camps that resembled very much their own. How, in another two weeks, they passed the same hill again, and the same set of camps. And how they realized, then, that these camps were indeed their very own; and the hill was the Pyramid Forty, and the river on which they were driving flowed, without inlet or outlet, in a circle around its base!

It is a good tale and, of all the Paul Bunyan stories, the one, I think, which is seasoned most strongly with the true flavor of the woods. It is a tale in which scholars detect the riverman's and shanty boy's endeavor to symbolize—and laugh away—the futility of their lives: the season of driving work, the hell-roaring bender, the vanished stake. A tale in which, perhaps, they laughed a little, also, at the ultimate futility of all human endeavor.

And perhaps the scholars are right. Perhaps Carl Sandburg is right when he says, "The people, the bookless people, they made Paul and had him alive long before he got into the books for those who read. He grew up in shanties, around the hot stoves of winter, among socks and mittens drying, in the smell of tobacco smoke and the roar of laughter mocking the outside weather." And perhaps that is the way Paul Bunyan, and Babe his great blue ox, and all the deadpan tales of wonder clustering about the fabulous pair, were actually born.

I do not know. I am no scholar, and I have only my own memory to serve me; but try as I may, I cannot recall any mention of Paul Bunyan at Dempsey's camp. Nor have I ever found a single old-time logger who can remember having heard a Paul Bunyan story as early as 1906.

The earliest reference to the mythical boss logger—by an authentic lumberjack—that I can recall was ten years later. And that, strangely enough, while made by a Minnesota lumberjack, recounted one of Paul's adventures in the Far West. It was a story, told to me by a teamster from Nester's camp on Lake Pequewam, about Paul's journey to the Pacific Coast: how, after many vicissitudes, Paul and Babe climbed, at last, to the summit of the Cascades and gazed down upon the blue waters of the West.

"And there, to be sure," said the story-teller, "they saw Old Puget building the Sound."

That was thirty years ago, and only after that, it seems to me, in the late evening of logging in the Great Lakes timberlands, did the Paul Bunyan stories become current in the camps. And then never as the long, elaborate tales that now fill so many books; but only as allusions and mentions of a brief, fragmentary, and usually unprintable nature.

Did a man in camp, for instance, limp? He had worked for Paul Bunyan on the Pyramid Forty—got that way, naturally, from walking round and round the hillsides. Was the weather cold? Well, maybe—but nothing like the Winter of the Blue Snow when the temperature dropped to forty feet below zero, and the loggers' cuss words froze —and then all thawed out at once in spring! Was a certain lake very round and deep? Paul Bunyan's bean hole, of course.

And thus only, in little snatches and sly references— accompanied always by a twinkle of the eye and the knowing look, more expressive than the words themselves—you gathered, here and there, the pieces of the whole tale. Little by little, if you had the memory and patience to put the pieces together, the saga of Paul Bunyan would come together for you, like one of those animated jig-saw diagrams on the screen.

But whether the fabulous stories of the Pyramid Forty, and the Winter of the Blue Snow, and the feats of Babe the Great Blue Ox were first told in print, as some claim, or whether they first spun themselves in the spoken word around the bunkhouse stove and campfire of the drive— that I must leave to the scholars.

II

You could tell a top loader by his footgear and the way he handled himself. He had no leather tops on his low rubber boots, because he had to be light and handy on his feet; and he moved about with the neat and poised grace of a riverman.

His job was much like a riverman's, at that—dancing about on logs all day, only the logs were high up on a loaded sleigh instead of in the water; and, like a riverman, he used a peavey in his work, instead of a canthook.

The top loader was boss of his loading crew, an engineer, architect and almost always a competent cusser, starting as he did with the advantages of strong lungs and a strident voice. Nor, since he was in almost continual peril of his life at the hands of his co-workers, did he often lack something to cuss about.

As soon as an empty sleigh pulled up alongside the skidway, the top loader and his crew of two senders-up, or "ground hogs," went into action. With canthooks they rolled the first log off the skidway onto the sleigh, centering it on the cross beams to "balance the bunk." And then began the exacting business of building the load. There were no side walls on a hauling sleigh; no stakes, even, to keep the logs from rolling off. There was nothing much to keep them securely in place as they moved, a towering mass, over miles of iced roads—nothing, that is, save the force of gravity and the skill of the loading crew.

Tier on tier, across the fourteen-foot bunks, the load built up. As it grew in height, the senders-up began to use a horse and loading chain to roll the logs up the inclined skids to the top of the load. Sometimes a log inadvertently went up endwise. This was called "gunning it," and was the occasion for some of the top loader's finest verbal achievements.

During the whole loading process, indeed, the top loader was an extremely active individual. With deft tugs and thrusts of his peavey he "settled" the logs into place; he directed the work of the ground crew; and all the while he contrived with a nonchalant air to avoid being crushed by the logs as they came "bowling up" the skids. And so, dancing like a puppet on strings atop his load, in continuous peril of his life, he built his load.

Halfway up, chains were thrown over the top and more logs put on until a height of ten feet or so had been reached. Then the whole load was encircled by a chain which was drawn taut; a few logs were placed on top, perhaps as binders. But the chains were a gesture, mostly; unless the load were properly built, solid and tight, it would "break," probably on a hay hill, and another teamster would go to town in a wooden box.

Ordinarly from 5,000 to 7,000 feet of logs would be put on a hauling sleigh: forty or fifty logs to a load. But occasionally a hauling crew—on a wager, for exhibition purposes, or merely for the hell of it—would turn in something really fancy in the way of loading.

The largest load I have ever heard of was one of 21,700 feet built by a loading crew at Lost Lake, Wisconsin, in 1906. It was nineteen feet wide and twenty-four feet high, and it was hauled three-quarters of a mile. Stewart Holbrook, in his excellent account of cross-continent logging, "Holy Old Mackinaw," however, reports on the "World's

Fair Load" of 1893, which scaled no less than 36,055 feet and was thirty feet in height!

At Camp Dempsey, Sandy MacDonald built a load of 18,754 feet, but it is little spoken of, for it tipped over on its way to the landing—a misfortune which Sandy, it appeared, attributed to the fact that the sleigh was painted blue. While this made little sense to anyone save Sandy, his remarks to Dempsey are a matter of unwritten record.

"You and your goddam blue sleigh," he said acidly, with strong and unaccountable emphasis on the *blue*.

III

Camp Dempsey
January 27, 1907

Dear Ma:

As today is Sunday, I am spending it in writing letters, and the first one is to you. It is a good day to stay inside— a cold, blustery day, with the snow blowing through the woods in great high, smoky clouds. But the sky is as blue as in June.

It is still awfully cold, and we have had many cases of frost-bite in camp. It is so cold that the axes often break in the men's hands. And if you touch one, your skin immediately freezes to the steel. But there is still no hard ice on the landing, because of the deep snow, and the loads sometimes break through. Then you should hear Dempsey cuss!

I hope you aren't having any trouble heating the house, Ma. Have Carlie keep it banked good and high with snow.

And tell him to use those birch logs, at the far end of the woodshed, to keep a fire overnight. I worry sometimes about how you are getting along, but I suppose Carlie is taking care of everything.

Yesterday I spent some of the morning visiting with Nels Lundell, the filer. He knew Pa—put in a winter with him on the Whiteface—and he told me about the time Pa helped to break the jam at Willow.

You would have enjoyed visiting Nels' cabin, Ma. He is a good housekeeper and his place is very neat and comfortable. He has a window over his bench, where he keeps the saws filed sharp for the sawing crews; a small air-tight, a pair of red Hudson's Bay blankets on his bunk, and a picture of King Oscar on the wall. His cabin is quite a center of camp gossip—as, I guess, the filer's shack always is.

Well, here comes Toivo Maki again. He has been in twice before this week to look at a pair of horsehide mittens he wants to buy. He can't seem to make up his mind. He just examines the mittens, then hands them back to me without a word. It has got so that, when I see Toivo coming, I automatically put the mittens out on the counter.

(P.S. He didn't buy them this time either.)

Ma, what do you think? I have met a very nice girl, way up here in the woods. Her name is Sari Luomala, and she has been teaching school at Mountain Iron. But she is with her father now, near Panger. I don't know her very well yet, but she asked me to stop at their place sometime when I am in Panger.

Ma, do you remember that copy of Lafcadio Hearn's "Some Chinese Ghosts"—it's in the bookcase in my room. I wonder if you could send it up to me? I'd like to give it to Sari to read.

Well, it won't be long before I'll be down now. (I still feel bad that I couldn't make it at Christmas.) Be careful of yourself and write again soon.

With love,

Matt

IV

At times it was necessary for Dempsey to write a letter to headquarters in Mokoman. On such occasions he spent some time working himself up to the creative pitch required for so important an act; and then, because he himself could write little more than his own signature, I did the job for him.

"Clerk," he would say at last, "will ye write down a letter."

He would begin to dictate, and at first very formally: "Mister C. N. Cobb, Zenith Lumber Company, Mokoman, Minnesota. Dear Sir—" A long pause, perhaps while he poked about in his beard. And, finally: "Referrin' to yers of th' twenty-first instant—"

But Dempsey rarely proceeded beyond that point in direct dictation.

"Listen, clerk," he would continue, his big face earnest with the labor of composition, "you tell them goddam thickheads down there, now—"

When I had finished taking notes on Dempsey's sul-

174

phuric remarks about the loading chain situation, I worked them up into a letter and read it to him. He would then probably say, "Well, it ain't jest the way I said it, but she'll do." And he would scrawl his P. Dempsey at the bottom of the sheet.

During January Dempsey wrote an uncommonly large number of uncommonly indignant letters to Mokoman on the subject of equipment and supplies; but, as so often happens, the correspondence seemed only to add bad feeling to confusion. Finally Dempsey abandoned all faith in the written word.

On the evening of January twenty-seventh, according to my diary, after he had returned from a visit to Tobin, he said abruptly, "Clerk, ye've got t' go down in the mornin'."

"To Mokoman?" I asked.

To Mokoman it was, right enough. Dempsey explained my mission. And then:

"Ye'd better take the gray and the jumper," he added. "Ye will save a day over goin' down with the tote-team."

I was too excited, I suppose, to pay much attention to the worried look in the boss' eyes. After awhile he asked:

"Have ye been over to Tobin lately, clerk?"

"No," I answered, hardly hearing him. "No, I haven't."

Dempsey was silent for a little time. He stooped over then, and began to unlace his boots.

"I don't like the looks of things over there," he said slowly.

V

We left camp in the steely light of early morning—
Cherry and I in the jumper.

I hadn't expected to have Cherry's company on that
trip, but there she was, nevertheless, snug under the buffalo robe and joggling against me as we lurched over the
tote-road.

She had been waiting for me when, having harnessed
the horse, I returned to the office for my papers. She was
sitting there in the shadows on the edge of my bunk,
dressed in her city clothes, button shoes and all, and with
her hair done up in a pompadour. She had tied a Paisley
scarf over her head and was holding her hat on her
drawn-up knees.

"Hello," she said casually. "Are we ready to go?"

"How did *you* get here?" I asked, startled and incredulous.

"Oh, I walked over," she said. "It wasn't bad. There's
been a full moon all night."

I looked, still unbelieving, at the valise on the floor
beside her.

"I carried that too," she said. "It wasn't so bad. Pat said
last night that you were going down this morning. I
thought I'd go with you."

"You must have decided in a hurry."

"I did."

She stood up, picked up the valise and looked at me
steadily, out of an almost expressionless face.

176

"If you'll just drop me off at Panger—" she said. "I'll catch the Dinkey."

"Oh, you're going to the Range?"

"Yes. Feel better?"

I did feel better. I was relieved that she wasn't going my way—to Mokoman; and I tried to make conversation as we drove out of camp. But suddenly Cherry became altogether uncommunicative.

Nearing Wolf Creek, we overtook a crew of men on their way to the landing, and they stood off the road to let us by. Among them was Gachot. He shouted something after us: what it was I couldn't make out, but the men with him burst into laughter. At the Wolf we left the tote-road and drove on the ice.

It was pleasant, after the ruts and pot holes, to follow the creek's smooth curves. The Wolf was a broad and gentle stream and so solidly frozen that we had to leave it only once, at the Ottertrack Rapids, where you could hear the muffled voice of hurrying water and sometimes glimpse it darkly through holes in the marshmallow-like snow. We jogged along at a steady pace, our frosty breaths pursuing us like wraiths on the still air.

"I'm not coming back," Cherry said suddenly, in a flat, peculiar tone.

I thought she meant that she wasn't coming back with me on my return.

"I'll be through Panger again on Friday," I said. "It'll be late, I expect, but if you like—"

"I'm not coming back at all."

"Oh," I said. "I hadn't heard."

"Nobody's heard. I just made up my mind. I just decided. I haven't told anybody—I want you to."

"Want me to what?"

"To tell them. Tell them I've gone—lit out—twenty-three skidoo."

"Don't your folks know?"

"Nobody knows. God damn it, I told you that," Cherry said impatiently.

"What—what are you going to do?" I asked.

If that's how things were, I thought, Jennie and Big Bill would like to know all about it. But Cherry made no answer. I glanced at her sidewise. She looked very pretty with the bright scarf over her hair, her cheeks freshened by the cold, her black eyes shining with moisture from the wind and looking straight ahead.

"Ted was home last week," she said.

I didn't say anything. I just waited, in a sort of embarrassed silence, for more to come. And it came presently, in a cold, flat rush of words.

"He was stinking drunk all the time," Cherry said. "It was the first time he's been home since he went up for Cordy in October. Ted and me have been married two years, almost, but I ain't seen him much. I ain't seen him sober hardly at all. Between the woods and the drives is all—and then he's plastered, most of the time.

"I guess you can't blame him," she said, and I felt that she was talking to herself rather than to me. "Ted's all right, I guess. But I've had enough. Last night I decided I had enough. Just made up my mind to hell with it. . . . It ain't Ted's drinkin' only—it's the god-damned woods.

Look at Ma. She's goin' crazy, finally. I knew she would some day."

"You don't mean—" I interrupted, shocked at what she was saying.

"Sure I mean it. You heard her yourself, didn't you—talkin' about greens all the time—singin' that song she made up? Ma's *sick*—sick in her mind. And who wouldn't be! . . . Twenty years, almost, in these lousy woods. Tryin' to keep Pa sober. Tryin' to keep Pa away from the drink—so's *he* won't kill nobody. Poor Pa . . ."

She became silent again, sitting very erect, looking straight ahead.

"Seems like kind of a bad time to be leaving her," I said.

"You didn't have to come out with that!" she flared up. "Pa'll take care of her. Ma'll be all right. Anyhow, she won't be any *worse* off—"

"What are *you* going to do?" I asked again.

"I don't know. Etta knows. Etta's my friend—in Eveleth. Maybe we'll go down to the Twin Cities. Maybe to Chicago or one of them places, even. We'll get jobs somewheres. We'll get along all right."

As we arrived at the railroad, Panger was just opening his store. The Dinkey would be along sometime during the day; Panger flagged it for passengers who wanted to get aboard there.

"Well," Cherry said, "I guess I'll go inside and keep warm."

I carried her valise over to the door of the store for her.

"When you see the folks," she said, "tell them I'll write.

You can tell them I won't be gone long—I just went on a visit, tell them. I'll write and let them know all about it."

She spoke very fast and her eyes, I was surprised to see, were filled with tears.

"I know you don't like me much," she said, "but it seems like I should say good-by to *someone* . . . on a trip like this."

Suddenly Cherry threw her arms about me and kissed me; her tears wet my face.

Not far beyond Panger, the Wolf emptied into the Ojibway—a smooth, white highway to the St. Pierre and Mokoman. As the gray jogged along, my thoughts swirled and scattered like the little clouds of snow racing across the river ice.

CHAPTER FIFTEEN

I

Nothing, one would suppose, could surpass the peaceful quiet of a logging camp at night: a camp securely battened down against the deep, still cold, its chimneys sending up their gently wavering strands of smoke to the silent stars; a camp lying snug beneath a two-foot coverlet of snow upon its roofs and nestled to its very eaves in shadowy drifts; a camp in whose deserted streets nothing alive would be astir, unless it were a visiting rabbit, perhaps, hopping jauntily along upon its padded feet. And yet it seems to me that something was forever happening at Dempsey's camp to disturb my sleep.

For a while it was young Jack McShane. McShane was a quiet-spoken, well-liked lad and a top loader of distinction. But when he arrived at Dempsey's camp, well toward the middle of the sawing season, he was in a piteous state with liquor. It was plain to see that he was on the edge of a complete breakdown, and every minute fighting a silent battle for control of himself. And there was fear in his eyes.

During the daytime it was not too bad; he could hold his own. But at night—at night there would be a knock on the office door and Dempsey would heave himself out of his bunk, growling and cursing as he fumbled with matches to light the lamp above my counter. Then he would open the door, and there would be standing young McShane, saying nothing, but with that fear in his eyes. I would see Dempsey then, in his long gray underwear, take a bottle from under the counter and very, very carefully—like a chemist measuring some liquid in a graduate —pour a drink for the boy. McShane would put it down, nod his thanks, and leave—but only to be back again, standing silently there in the doorway, maybe once more, or even twice, before morning.

But after a while he "came to call on us," as Dempsey euphemistically put it, only once a night—usually around three o'clock in the morning—and each time for a little shorter drink; until, at last, he came no more, and Dempsey and I would have slept peacefully through the nights —if it had not been for Adam Peters.

Adam was the scaler at Dempsey's camp and, of course, lived with us in the office. He was a small, respectable-looking man, quite bald but possessing, in compensation, a large walrus mustache. Adam had a family in Mokoman, and everybody said wasn't it a pity—what they had to put up with. For Adam also was a drinking man.

His drinking was on a different order, however, from McShane's. Adam had been steadily, if mildly, drunk for years. He arrived in camp with the first Poirer packsack I ever saw; and this packsack, under a layer of clothing, was filled with Old Crow whiskey. Thus, dropping casually into the office now and then for a little something against the cold, he was enabled to maintain his accustomed level of consumption.

Save, perhaps, for a certain melancholy vagueness in his pale blue eyes, this steady intake of liquor appeared to have no effect upon the quiet, sweet-tempered little man. But retribution, when it came, was sudden—and startling.

One night I was awakened by cries overhead. They came from the bunk above mine, where Adam at the time slept with one Ole Petersen, a horse doctor. They were animal-like cries of terror, and of such great volume that it seemed impossible that Adam could have emitted them. They awakened Dempsey, of course, who sat up and bellowed, "What the hell goes on here?" Then Petersen, jumping up so suddenly that he knocked his head against a roof rafter, added his yowls of pain to the general din. After that it was very difficult to return to sleep.

In some ways the events of several nights later were even more nerve-wracking. On this occasion I was awakened by someone cautiously climbing down the cornerpost from the bunk above. It was Adam, and he walked, very quietly and with a peculiar, gingerly step, toward the center of the room. There he paused and, in his gray flannel shirt and baggy drawers, stood in the moonlight that filtered through the frosted window panes. His head inclined intently toward the floor, and his gaze appeared to follow the movements of something at his feet. Now he advanced a little and stooped to examine more closely whatever it was his eyes were seeing. Now he retreated skittishly, as if to avoid stepping on something. His audience—Dempsey, Petersen and I—watched him in fascinated silence. Dempsey was the first to break the spell that seemed to hold us all immobile.

"D' ye see 'em, Adam? D' ye see 'em?" he asked softly from his bunk.

"By the livin' Christ, I see 'em!" bellowed Adam in an unexpectedly loud voice.

He stood for a few moments blinking owlishly at us; then, without further words, he climbed back into his bunk and went to sleep.

Partly by the circumstance of his running out of whiskey, Adam was forced to leave us shortly thereafter, and things were relatively quiet, except for Axel Gunderson. Axel was "more horse than human," Dempsey said. Occasionally when he harnessed Dempsey's big gray to the jumper, he did not bother to put on his shoes (if he happened to be summoned from his siesta) but pranced about bare-footed in the snow.

When the cold became really bitter in January, Axel, then the bull-cook, was charged with the important duty of keeping the camp stoves going throughout the night. Exactly how he stoked the office stove, I do not know, but my impression at the time was that he stood at a distance and heaved great tamarack logs into the open door. At any rate, the procedure was accompanied by a most alarming series of bumps, thumps, crashes and bangs.

This situation Dempsey endeavored to correct by patiently explaining to Axel that, what with one thing and another, we hadn't been getting much sleep in the office lately, and would he for Christ's sake try to fill the stove without knocking the goddam place down on our heads, or would he like to have his thick hide taken off, maybe?

And Axel, it must be said in his behalf, tried mightily thereafter to perform his duties quietly, advancing daintily to the stove with a huge billet of firewood in his arms and easing it into the door as gently as a mother tucking away her babe. Not infrequently, however, he would make some slight sound in spite of himself. Thereupon, filled with self-reproof, he would break our sleep with muttered imprecations which registered, I am sure, only a few decibels less than the bellowings of a bull.

So passed the long winter nights at Dempsey's camp. Now and then a cougar, nosing about in the timber, contributed to the din with its blood-chilling screams—surely one of the most alarming sounds ever heard by man. Throughout the January cold spell the pines and spruces, frozen to their very cores, exploded with loud reports, like rifles fired by invisible skirmishers in the night. And once Dempsey himself shattered sleep when he sat bolt upright in his blankets and yelled in the loudest roar I have ever heard: "Stand, you son-of-a-bitch!" He had dreamed, so he said, that a man was coming at him, rifle in hand, through the open doorway.

But perhaps I exaggerate. Quite possibly my memory makes too much of incidents such as these, weighing them too heavily against the quiet, snow-bound nights disturbed only by Dempsey's occasional snores and the comfortable crackle of the tamarack fire—nights through which I slumbered peacefully and well.

February 3rd

Today being Sunday, and an extraordinarily cold one (the thermometer this morning stood at 42 degrees below zero), most of the crew stuck close to the stoves and the camp was very quiet.

Dempsey went over to Tobin and came back this evening rather gruff. Apparently Jennie and Big Bill are pretty cut up about Cherry. They haven't had any word from her yet, and Dempsey said that Jennie is acting "queer." He didn't explain what he meant.

February 5th

Spent most of this afternoon with the smith—sometimes called the "ironburner"—going over his stocks and making out a re-order list. The smith (Pete Coffee) has one adjective, "sonofabitchin," which he applies to everything and everyone—especially the handy-man.

Pete and the handy-man work together in a log building with a shanty roof, two small windows, and a cast iron stove to keep them warm. The smithy is equipped with a forge, an anvil and a horse-shoeing outfit. About the only materials the smith has to work with are round and flat iron bars of various dimensions. From these he fabricates everything, even bolts and nuts.

The handy-man, who has his own set of tools, must hew whatever lumber he needs out of trees—for none is carried in stock. He has a bench in the smith's shanty and uses the latter's vise, an arrangement that seems to cause a good many squabbles between them.

Nobody knows just why the smith and the handy-man get along so badly. Some think their quarrel goes back to the time, early in the winter, when a wildcat got into the smith's shanty and the handy-man, escaping first, slammed the door in his excitement on the smith—and the cat.

III

As I urged Dempsey's gray over the Corey-Nixon road, west of Panger, we traversed, I suppose, some of the most desolate cutover lands ever left behind by logging crews. It was a desolation that not even the great snows of 1906 could conceal.

On both sides of the road, fire, like a hungry jackal, had followed the loggers. It had licked over the slashings with its black tongue and had withered the tall birch forests with its poisonous breath; the stark cadavers of the birches stood rotting inside their silver skins, soft and punky— you could push them over with your hands.

But what was left of the pines did not rot. The stumps and slashings, for some strange reason, refused to decay and merge again with the forest floor. All the untidy debris of logging merely bleached and hardened, and became a tangle of bare and weathered stumps, trunks and branches, as indestructible, it seemed, as the glacial boulders strewn among them.

Only the Finns had the courage—or, as most said, the foolhardiness—to undertake the clearing and farming of such forsaken lands. Only the Finns, it was said, spoke a language the stumps could understand.

Sari Luomala had said that theirs was the second farmstead beyond the crossing at Panger; but we must have gone almost a mile, the gray and I, before we came to it, a small clearing in the cutover occupied by several log buildings.

Nearest the road stood the dwelling house, built of squared and whitewashed logs; it had a vaguely foreign look, due perhaps to the blue-painted door and the blue window frames. For luck a rowan tree—called mountain ash in Minnesota—had been planted near the doorway.

Clustered back of the house were the barn, a few outbuildings—one of which, no doubt, was a *sauna*, or Finnish steam bath—and a couple of gum-drop hay stacks. The place had the bleak and lonely look of all such homesteads in the stump lands.

I turned in and hitched the horse to an aspen tree near the house. My heart, I remember plainly, beat a little faster than usual as I knocked on the blue—a strong Finnish blue—door.

It opened immediately and Sari stood in the doorway. My sudden appearance must have caused her some mild surprise, for she stood looking at me for a moment as one might look at a neighbor's child paying one an unexpected visit. Then, smiling with her strange star sapphire eyes, she asked me eagerly to come in.

"It's *you!*" she exclaimed. "I didn't think you would come. I hoped you would—but I didn't expect it, really. *Please* come in."

188

"I was in Panger—" I stammered.

"How nice! You are just in time to have some lunch with us."

The house was fragrant with warm, appetizing kitchen smells—a fresh baking, coffee, pans of new milk on the table. On the table, too, were several blue crockery bowls filled with something that looked like thick cream, a plate of dark bread, and another of pale butter scooped generously from the firkin.

I said I would stay, and Sari smiled happily. Inclining her head toward a man sitting with thin, folded hands in a rocking chair beside the stove, she said with a little gesture:

"This is my father. I have told him all about you. Father, this is Matt."

The man gave me the slow smile of the sick and murmured something I could not catch. He had a lean, sparsely bearded face with an almost Tartaric cast; it must have possessed a kind of fierce ruggedness when he was well.

"My father speaks English," Sari explained. "But it is hard for him to talk now."

She made up a tray of food and placed it on a chair beside the sick man. He smiled and patted her hand.

I watched Sari as she moved deftly about the room. It was a simple, even a poor room; but there was nothing mean or dejected in its poorness. On the contrary, it shone with a passionate neatness and respectability. You could see it in the adzed log walls, spotless and smooth as plaster with many coats of whitewash; in the polished kitchen

189

range and the gleaming dishpan on the wall behind it; in the crisp laundered look of the rag rugs on the painted floor. The room was divided by a partition of bare pine boards, on which hung a large, elaborately framed photograph of a woman who, in a remote spectral way, resembled Sari. And there was little else to relieve its severity save a bright woven coverlet on a cot—brought perhaps from "the Old Country"—and some nuggets of Lake Superior copper neatly arranged on a shelf beside an imitation marble mantel clock.

But Sari, like those serene women in the little genre paintings of the Dutch, imparted by the simple fact of her presence a particular dignity and grace to the humble backwoods interior. She placed one of the blue bowls before me and seated herself at the table.

"Have some *viiliä*," she said. "Have you ever tried it?"

I said I hadn't, and dipped into the bowl curiously with a large iron spoon. Under the crinkly yellow layer of clotted cream, I discovered, was a sort of clabber. I did not relish its sharp, acid taste.

"I can see you don't like the *viiliä*," Sari said. "Well, don't eat it. I'll get you something else."

But I protested that I did like it and succeeded in getting it all down, together with several slices of bread and butter. It was better as you got used to it.

"When you eat *viiliä*—and like it," Sari observed, "people who don't eat *viiliä* think you are queer. They think you are funny somehow—and not as good as they are. That's all some people have to feel superior about—things like eating *viiliä*. Well, *I* like it."

190

Sari, I found, had opinions on a great many subjects and, in a time when girls were not supposed to think, she expressed them with a sometimes startling directness.

"*Oma tupa, oma lupa*—do you know what that means?" she asked. "Of course, you don't. I'll tell you. It means, 'One's own cabin, one's own freedom.' You think we Finns are foolish to grub our lives away among these stumps—"

She looked at me steadily, smiling, childlike with her fresh-scrubbed face and the dark braids curving over her breasts.

"But we—we Finns think you are the foolish ones," she said, "wearing out your lives for the big bosses. They value you no more than animals. Kusti Lahti, our neighbor, took his horse with him when he went to work in Haney's camp. His horse earned more than he did!"

She gazed at me with incredulous eyes.

"Imagine that—the beast worth more than the master!"

I stirred uncomfortably. Nobody in Mokoman talked that way about the Companies. It was the way those "parlor socialists" were talking out East. It was like being an atheist, almost.

"Only when you get old or crippled, they don't shoot you—like a horse," Sari said. "They just say, 'Good-by—we don't want you any more. Go home!'"

Sari's father, I learned, had for several years published a newspaper on the Range. But he was an indifferent business man and the venture was unsuccessful; so, responding, perhaps, to a deep, traditional Finnish urge, he had "taken to the land." Since 1903 he and a few other home-

191

steaders had struggled along, with incredible toil and hardship, in the hitherto unpenetrated cutover area around Panger, just as other groups of Finns were already settling in the equally remote Palo-Makinen and Brimson-Toimi districts.

But Heikki Luomala had not ceased to think while he cleared the land of stumps and rocks, or even to read a little. And it was from him, plainly, that Sari had got a way of looking at things which was surprising, if not downright disconcerting, in a girl of her milieu.

After lunch we chatted about the people we knew in Mokoman, and about the goings-on in the high school there. Sari told me about the gay *laskianen*, the Shrovetide coasting parties, which the Finns at Toivolo, where she had once taught school, gave each winter; and I described the Prom and the football rallies at the university. I gave her my copy of *Some Chinese Ghosts*, which I had almost forgotten I had brought for her; and her eyes lighted with excitement as she looked through it. And so we talked for awhile about books, and several times Sari mentioned the *Kalevala*.

"What," I asked her, "is the *Kalevala?*"

I asked the question casually—casually and stupidly and with unconscious arrogance . . . as though anything of Finnish origin could possibly be of much importance!

I might have detected a flicker of incredulity in Sari's eyes, but she gave no sign of annoyance. She told me about the *Kalevala*, instead: how it had been made by the people and sung by them for many generations; how it had never been written down, even, until very recently; how the Finns loved it so much that even in the rude cutover settlements it was not unusual to find a farmer who knew it and could recite it. Her father, Sari said, knew much of the poem by heart, and she herself could give long passages from it—especially from the Song of Aino, which was her favorite.

She repeated some of it in the liquid, musical syllables of the Finnish, and then she translated as best she could from memory. I cannot, of course, recall her very words, but I now have the printed verses in English, and they are much as I remember Sari reciting them, a little haltingly, in her fresh, gentle voice:

> "Hung her ribbons on the aspen,
> Left her gold-cross on the sea shore,
> Silken robes upon the alders,
> On the rocks her silken stockings,
> On the grass her shoes of deer skin,
> In the sand her shining necklace,
> In the sand her rings and jewels,
> In the waves the lovely Aino
> Sleeping on the very bottom
> Of the deep and boundless blue sea,
> In the caverns of the salmon,
> There to be the whitings' sister,
> And the friend of nimble fishes. . . ."

On the long drive back to Dempsey's fragments of Aino's song returned over and over with a strange insistence, to my curiously excited memory. But still more vividly returned the sweet cadence of Sari's words, the way her mouth formed to make the odd Finnish vowels, and the little flame that seemed to light in her shadowy eyes as she retold Aino's sad and lovely story.

193

CHAPTER SIXTEEN

I

*T*HERE ARE many kinds of snows, and we had them all during the winter of 1906-7. They lay one over the other like geologic strata, up to the very eaves of our camps; they covered the lakes so heavily that the ice underneath refused to make; they were the deepest and the meanest snows in the memory of our crew.

Continuously from the middle of October until the month of April, snow came down upon us and piled up around us; or so it seemed during those long, dark days. For almost six months we lived in a world of unremitting whiteness—a world that, sometimes in subtle, sometimes in dramatic ways, remade and reshaped itself after each great snowfall.

Perhaps the snow would come down gently, like a quiet white rain, descending vertically and accumulating flake by flake on the ground, the trees, and all horizontal surfaces—until the whole earth was covered with a soft *poured* whiteness of rounded curves and gentle forms. Then it would lie heavy on every branch and every tree trunk that sloped even a little from the perpendicular; it would lie in great slabs on flat places, such as shanty roofs and the icing tank; it would cap each stump in the cutover so that they resembled gigantic mushrooms; and it would overhang the roofs of our camps and pile up against our windows in ice-edged drifts. The small pines, weighted down with the burden of this snow, would droop dejectedly, bowing to each other like dancers in a sad and frosty quadrille. And shortly, throughout the still forest, the snow would begin to tumble from the branches, dropping silently and continuously in powdery, drifting clouds from the taller pines.

These were mostly the early snows. The later ones—the tremendous, unprecedented falls of January—came to us on the icy north and northwest winds, and they drove down on us like blasts of alabaster sand. They whirled in tiny twisters across the frozen drifts and blew in clouds from the roofs of our camps. And then they lay upon the ground in sharply sculptured drifts, sometimes in the windswept places ribbed like the sand on a seashore. Your footsteps in such snow made clean, deep, azure-filled holes.

Many other kinds of snow fell during that long, deep winter in the woods: those that came down in February and melted almost at once, edging our eaves with massive icicles and fringing the·underside of every branch like a crystal hunting shirt; the snows of early January that froze to a solid crust, strong enough to bear a man, and glistened like white glare-ice in the moonlight and in the late or early sun; and the soft, lovely snows that fell in great six-pointed feather flakes, and covered the earth with celestial fleece.

In endless succession all these snows fell, layer on layer,

until the pathways dug through the drifts resembled tunnels, and it seemed as if the whole world would be overwhelmed in a great white deluge. Until far into the month of May, they remained in the valleys and swamps.

But if the winter of 1906-7 was memorable for its snows, it was also long remembered for its extreme cold. During January of that year, our thermometer at Dempsey's registered well below zero for the thirty-one successive days. At times it fell to 48 degrees below zero—80 degrees below freezing, Fahrenheit!

In such cold, even though you wore two suits of heavy woolen underwear and three pairs of socks with sheepskin inner-soles, the danger of frostbite, or worse, was real and constant. At the skidways and on the landing you could make a fire to beat off the cold a little; if you were a teamster you could jog along beside your load to keep your circulation going; and, whenever you could, you sought the shelter of the woods. Yet, despite all your precautions, an ear, a section of your face, or your nose might turn a livid white; and, unless someone told you about it, and you rubbed the place promptly and vigorously with snow, you were in for trouble.

In such cold, the smoke from our fires condensed immediately and rolled down into the camp street, there to lie in heavy clouds. The pines and spruces froze to their very cores, splitting and exploding with loud reports; and the axes we used against them sometimes broke like glass. The snow, in those temperatures, shrieked underfoot and beneath the iron runners of the sleighs. The world flashed crimson when you blinked your eyes, and the salt tears froze and stuck your lids together; and the frozen snow, whipping against your eyeballs, was a grave and ever present menace.

It was in January that a phenomenon, never before seen by anyone at Camp Dempsey, appeared in the sky: a paraselene, a great, misty circle around the sun, quartered by lines of light, and with a large sun-dog at each intersection of lines and circle.

This, in the crew's estimation, was second in awesomeness only to another occurrence which took place at about the same time: on two separate days during January, so intense was the cold that Dempsey suspended work in the woods and kept the crew under cover in the bunkhouse. It was, all agreed, a damned cold winter!

II

You thought at once of a circus elephant teetering along on a row of overturned tubs; and a full load of logs, piled ten feet high and sixteen wide, must have weighed as much as a good-sized elephant at that.

It was hard to believe, even when you saw it being done, that such a huge burden could be drawn for miles by two horses; and you were always a little afraid that it would crush the fragile sleigh upon which it was balanced, just as you always half-expected the elephant to stave in the tubs. But it was a cunningly wrought vehicle, the hauling sleigh, and I have never heard of one collapsing under its tremendous load.

Nobody, I suppose, can say who designed the hauling

sleigh. In its perfected form, as we knew it at Dempsey's, it was most likely a collaboration of many a woods boss, handy-man and hauling teamster, with perhaps a few sky-hookers' ideas tossed in for extra measure. And it is doubtful whether a whole drafting-roomful of modern engineers could have turned out a better job.

Its secret was in its flexibility. It had absolutely no fixed parts: everything moved, almost everything "gave," and the entire vehicle, conforming subtly to the movement of the load and the irregularities of the road, *absorbed* strains and stresses which it could never have resisted.

On such a sleigh—a loose organization of relatively fragile moving parts—a two-horse team could haul, and regularly did haul, from 5,000 to 7,000 feet of logs—as many as seventy logs to the load, weighing up to *thirty-five* tons. And, had necessity required it, twice that much, I am sure, could have been managed. For there was nothing a loading crew would not cheerfully undertake, if challenged; and what hauling skinner would hesitate to move anything the loaders might succeed in piling on his sleigh!

At Dempsey's camp we had six hauling sleighs constantly carrying logs from the skidways to the landing on Loon Lake. Because our haul was long and the road a little difficult in spots, each sleigh was drawn by a four-horse team.

The teamsters were among the highest paid men in camp. For not only was the job of skinning four horses over an icy road an exacting one, but even by the rigorous standards of the woods, it was hard work. The teamster was up long before daylight; he was the first to leave for "the works" in the morning, the last to come into the men's camp at night. He well earned his handsome forty dollars a month.

Nor was his work without hazard. Mostly the peril was on the hay hills. There, for all the watchfulness of the hill men, who strewed hay or sand in the sleigh ruts to retard its speed, the great load of logs might gather momentum; and the horses, struggling to hold it back, might, despite their sharpened shoes, lose footing and go down in a turmoil of threshing legs and rearing heads beneath an avalanche of logs.

Or, too much sand on a hill, or an overlooked bit of stone, might bring disaster. For then the king bolt, the one weak detail in the cunningly devised mechanism of the sleigh, might snap under the weight suddenly thrown against it, and several tons of logs would be catapulted upon horses and driver.

Yet, in spite of all its hardships and dangers, the job of hauling teamster was one many men aspired to in the woods—few, however, so fervently as did Ole Halvorsen.

Ole, a melancholy skidder, suddenly went "haywire" one day, as men sometimes did in the woods, and especially Scandinavians. He appeared at the office, a wild light in his blue eyes, toying significantly with a double-bitted ax.

"Aye vould like to drive eight horses," he announced somberly.

Dempsey poked a finger into his beard and gazed thoughtfully at the big skidder's ax.

"So ye'd like to drive eight horses, would ye, Ole?" he said soothingly. "Well, that's fine, now, that's fine. Of course I'm not needin' a eight-horse teamster meself—"

"Aye vant to drive eight-horse team," said Ole emphatically.

"To be sure, to be sure," said Dempsey hastily, never taking his eyes from Ole's ax. "And that ye can. Didn't I hear just today, now, that Terry Lynch is lookin' fer a eight-horse teamster? And ain't ye just the feller fer the job?"

"Aye vant to—"

"Tell ye what t' do," said Dempsey briskly. "Get yerself a good sleep t' night, Ole, and in the mornin' ye can go down with Ed on the tote team. He'll drop ye off at Terry's. Just tell him I sent ye. Tell Terry I sent ye to drive eight horses fer him."

Dempsey beamed happily at Ole.

"Terry," he said, "will be glad to see ye."

Ole considered the proposition morosely for a while, then he grunted appreciatively.

"Tanks, boss," he said. "Aye go down with Ed in morning."

"By the way, Ole," Dempsey said, "what the hell is a skinner—a eight-horse skinner, at that—totin' around a ax fer—like some goddam swamper?"

He held out his hand and Ole sheepishly surrendered the ax.

"Tanks, boss," he said again, and went out.

Dempsey ran his finger around the inside of his collar.

"Clerk," he said, "where's that bottle of whiskey? The push of this here camp needs a drink."

200

III

The conversation in the office, like that in the bunk-house, turned often on the subject of women. It was, however, on a somewhat higher level; and, on one occasion I can recall, it attained a special and particular kind of dignity.

That was the time that Dempsey made the statement that he had never seen his wife in the nude.

To the handful of loggers gathered around the office stove this presented an idea so novel as to be awesome. It was a matter for much speculation and reflection, all of a most respectful nature. And in time it became part of the Dempsey legend.

IV

In the evenings, after supper, the undercutters and the swampers sharpened their axes. The grindstones were in a corner of the bunkhouse and, since there were only two, the men would sometimes have to wait until ten o'clock for a chance at the stone.

You used to hear stories about lumberjacks shaving with their axes, and I suppose it could have been done. For the men laid their blades against the turning stone with the delicate touch of a barber honing a Swedish razor; and the edges they put on the steel were almost razor sharp.

The double-bitted ax, as it had evolved by Camp Dempsey's day, was an implement of graceful beauty—light, clean-lined, and, in the hands of an expert axman like Jake Powers or Mike Houle, a cutting tool of marvelous precision and efficiency. In appearance it recalled the two-edged battle-ax of ancient times. Its flat and rather thin head, weighing from three to four and a half pounds, was fitted to a light, straight hickory or ash helve; and when you hefted it, you could feel in your arms and fingers the sweetness of its design and balance. The heavy, clumsy single-edged ax of an earlier period—still used along the Atlantic seaboard—bore no more resemblance to this trim and beautiful instrument than did the Brown Bess musket, in a yet earlier day, to the Kentucky rifle.

In the New England camps trees were felled with the ax alone. Although the crosscut saw had long been used for "bucking" trees into log lengths, it was only at a relatively late date that it was introduced for felling, and many have wondered that such an obviously practical step should have been so long delayed. The answer, perhaps, is to be found in something as simple as the woodsman's love of the ax—and pride in his axman's skill.

The ax of today has degenerated, for the most part, into a tool with which farmers and small town householders split firewood, with which summer campers cut down and mutilate small trees. And one who has observed it only in such hands can hardly conceive of the effortless speed and efficiency with which a good undercutter—or perhaps two of them with alternate strokes—could perform a job of ax-work on a standing pine. Such a man could fell a 100-foot tree in its own shadow and, by the cunning of his ax, could "jump" it three feet from the stump. This he could do without a wasted stroke or unnecessary chip; and the kerf of his ax, he might admit, would be "as smooth as a baby's bottom." Is it difficult to understand such a man's reluctance to abandon his ax for a more efficient but less soul-satisfying method of whacking down trees?

V

One evening, about a week after I had returned from my trip to Mokoman, Joe Gachot came into the office. He opened the fresh box of snuff I had just handed him, and tucked a load into his lower lip. The lip protruded like a deformity, and when Gachot spoke you could see the dark tobacco lying there against his teeth. He screwed the top back on and leaned across the counter in an elaborately confidential manner.

"Have a good time in town?" he asked in a guarded voice.

He accompanied the question with a knowing look, half smirk, half leer.

"I spent all day at the office," I said, puzzled, "if you call that a good time."

"Yeh," Gachot said understandingly. "How was th' trip?"

"It was all right." I turned away and started to straighten up the shelves.

"Girl didn' come back with ya, did she?"

Had Gachot struck me with something from behind,

the effect, I suppose, would have been about the same.

"What do you mean by that?" I demanded.

Gachot backed away a little, but he made no answer. He merely shrugged indifferently.

"You dirty bastard," I said slowly and, hard as I struggled to control it, my voice shook. "Just what are you driving at?"

Gachot made a couple of *tsks* and looked at me reprovingly.

"Don't get excited, kid," he said. "And don't get me wrong. I don't give a good goddam if ya go t' town with a dozen wimmin. I ain't insinuatin'. I'm just lettin' ya know what's bein' peddled around."

He lowered his voice again to an intimate undertone.

"Let ya know somethin' else," he murmured reflectively. "Ted Gordon's one tough son-of-a-bitch."

Gachot apparently thought it unnecessary to elaborate on that statement. No doubt he considered its implications clear enough.

"Don't forget to put me down fer th' snoose," he said softly, and left.

CHAPTER SEVENTEEN

I

AN ARM of the great Tamarack Swamp reached into one end of the valley in which the Luomala farmstead lay—an estuary of a vast bog so extensive that no one knew for sure where its ultimate boundaries were. No one had ever crossed the swamp, or even penetrated it very far. It was mysterious and forbidding, as an inland sea would be that nobody had ever sailed.

Nothing lived in the swamp, except mice, red squirrels and chipmunks, and the hawks that wheeled in search of them, and many rabbits. Sari snared the rabbits for food, and one Sunday morning, late in January, I accompanied her while she set her snares.

Just out of sight of the farmstead we left the Corey-Nixon road, following a drift-obliterated logging road for perhaps a mile northward. Then Sari turned into a still narrower trail and presently we entered the swamp.

It was like going into a vast kind of building, almost. There was a feeling of shelter there, as though a roof were over the dim-lit spaces between the shadowy masses of tamarack and black spruce. A feeling of shelter and deep, silent peace where the snow lay undisturbed, soft-contoured beneath the trees.

"Look—do you see?" asked Sari. She pointed to a narrow pathway, not more than a hand's breadth wide, that crossed our own. "That's where the rabbits go. You'll see lots more pretty soon."

I observed how, as we pushed deeper into the great swamp, the rabbit runs did increase in number. They criss-crossed beneath the snow-laden branches of the trees. They became an intricate system of highways, with branch roads leading from every direction into the wider, harder-packed main thoroughfares.

"Well, here we are," said Sari. "Here's the place. Look how they run around here."

All the rabbit runs of the surrounding forest, indeed, seemed to converge at this one place. The snow was beaten hard, and littered with the clean, tan pellet-like droppings of the little animals.

"Can't you just see them hopping around here on a cold, bright night?" asked Sari, crinkling up her nose. "You never see them in the daytime—so it must be at night they have their meetings. Or whatever it is they do here."

"Maybe they come to church," I suggested. "There's the pulpit over there—that old stump."

"No, they wouldn't sit still long enough to hear the sermon. Rabbits are always running. Especially on real cold nights. I always get more in the snares then."

She reached into the pocket of her *capote* and drew out some coils of wire, the kind that is used for hanging pictures, soft and flexible, but strong.

"Do you want to help me with the snares?" she asked.

206

"I'll show you how." She offered me a two-foot length of wire with a loop at one end.

"Make the loop about as big as your fist. No, as big as *my* fist. There. Now bend the wire a little, so the loop won't slide shut. Make a kink in it. That's right."

I followed directions with chilled, unmittened fingers.

"Now," continued Sari, "we hang the loop from a good strong branch over the rabbit run. And when Mr. Rabbit comes along—whoosh! he gets caught. Like that." She shot her small fist through the noose, and the wire tightened about her wrist. "Come on, I'll show you."

We waded through the deep snow, sinking thigh-deep into the spongy muskeg moss that underlay it. Sari stopped several times to examine possible snare sites. Finally she dropped to both knees.

"Here's a good place," she called. "Be careful where you step, now."

I eased myself into the snow beside her and watched, fascinated, as her deft fingers adjusted the loop over the runway, smoothed it into a perfectly round, shining circle, and fastened it securely to the projecting branch of a fallen tamarack.

"You see?" she commented. "Not too high, or he will jump over it. Not too low, or he will run under it. Just about—here."

I laughed: she was so industrious and business-like about it, so serious. When I arose, she was so small down there at my feet—like a little boy in a bright red coat. After she had pulled on her mittens, I reached down and helped her up.

"So when he comes scooting along tonight—whoosh! he's caught. Say, this is real sport. Let me do the next one."

Sari straightened and brushed the powdery snow from her trousers. She shook her head.

"No, it's not sport at all, Matt. It's cruel. Sometimes they are still alive when I pick up my snares. They are so frightened—nothing can be so frightened as a rabbit. Fright will kill them sometimes. They kick up the snow all around, and sometimes they cry. Have you ever heard a rabbit cry, Matt? Then I have to hit them on the nose with a stick. That's not much fun—but it's one way to get food."

Something in the way she said this, looking at me with her cool, gray eyes, seemed to add, "But *you* wouldn't understand about that, I guess."

"How many do you think we'll catch?" I asked hastily.

"Oh, I don't know. If we set all twenty snares, maybe three or four. Or half a dozen, perhaps. You never can tell." She set out again through the deep snow, and I trudged after her.

"Once there was a boy lived next door to us in Mahtowa," she added irrelevantly, "who used to catch so many that he had his whole woodshed full of rabbits. He had them piled up like stove wood, clear to the roof—hundreds of frozen rabbits."

It was early afternoon when we had set all of the snares and stopped for lunch. We found a sheltered place where the snow had drifted cosily over a fallen spruce to form a windbreak. I knocked some limbs from a tree and, while

Sari unpacked the knapsack, started a little fire; soon a small pail of coffee was bubbling deliciously, and the sandwiches were toasting by the flames.

"Do you want me to make a charm against frozen hands?" Sari asked, holding her own slim fingers toward the fire to extinguish the cold that had suddenly nipped them.

"Sure," I said. "Make a good one."

"All right," she laughed. "I will. Maybe it will help while we eat."

Her voice took on a sing-song, ritualistic cadence and her small, cold-reddened face became serious, even though her eyes smiled, while she intoned:

> "Cold, thou son of Wind,
>   Do not freeze my finger nails,
>   Do not freeze my hands;
>   Freeze thou the water willows,
>   Go chill the birch chunks."

Sari laughed a small, musing laugh.

"They've got charms for everything in the Old Country," she said. "Their lives are very hard over there—I guess the charms help some."

We talked about the Old Country a little, while we ate our lunch. We built up the fire and sat beside it for a long time, talking about ourselves mostly. Dusk was gathering when we tossed the remnants of our sandwiches to a pair of melancholy whiskey jacks and fastened on our skiis for the homeward trek.

Les Crosby came into the office one evening to ask Dempsey's permission to go down to Mokoman. Les said he had to pay his lodge dues. Also, his sister's husband had shot a livery stable man in the City. Besides, his kidneys hadn't been functioning very well since he ate the balsam gum to cure his boils, and maybe he'd better see a doctor about it.

All this seemed to confuse Dempsey pretty thoroughly, for he grumbled his permission, and Les went down with Ed Benson the next morning. He took with him a good deal of the crew's cash for various purchases, and half a dozen watches in need of repair.

A watch was usually the first thing a lumberjack bought when he came down from the woods with a stake. And the fancier the locomotive or "stag at eve" on the case, the better. The insides didn't matter so much; hence a lumberjack's watch seldom kept ticking through a winter in the camps.

I often wondered about this obsession of loggers for watches. It is strange that men to whom time meant so little should have valued timepieces so highly. Perhaps the watch was to them a sort of symbol of escape from a timeless existence. Or maybe it was the nearest thing to something *permanent* a lumberjack could conceive of owning. Or perhaps it was just the idea of getting dressed up in a new fifteen dollar suit with a gold watch and chain, that got them.

Les Crosby, at any rate, took a good many dollars'

worth of watches with him, and considerable cash besides —most of it, as I have said, for various small purchases. Les wrote it all down on a piece of paper; and that is all the record anybody made.

Then he disappeared as completely and mysteriously as Houdini's elephant. The day on which he was scheduled to return dawned and turned to night. So did a dozen other days. Some of the men began to worry a little—not so much about their watches or money, as about Les. When a full two weeks had passed, however, the whole thing began to look a little queer, even to Les' best friends.

"He'll be back all right," Phil Leonard assured the doubters "—if he's still alive."

But that was precisely what worried some of the crew, and it worried them increasingly for almost a month. Then, quite as suddenly and unceremoniously as he had departed, Les returned from Mokoman. Only he had never been in Mokoman. He had gone straight to the City, instead; and there, with rude dispatch, they had thrown him into jail.

Les was not very clear as to just why he had been sent to the workhouse, but he said it wasn't much fun. All they gave him to eat, he said, was turnips, and sure enough, he did have a pretty pale and peaked turnip-diet look about him.

Les brought back all the watches, properly repaired, and every purchase he had been delegated to make. He took care of all that, he explained tersely, before he went on his bender. Mrs. Burns, who ran the boarding house for loggers in the city, had put everything in her safe and kept it for him. He seemed surprised that anyone should have imagined any other possibility.

The workhouse turnip diet, Les reported, appeared to have cured his kidney trouble.

III

We landed on Loon Lake. Some logging camps landed on rivers, but we put our cut into a lake. It was all the same. A stream ran out of Loon, a small river called the Little Sioux; and the Little Sioux emptied into the Ojibway, and the Ojibway into the St. Pierre which flowed through Mokoman, some seventy-five miles away.

That's the way the logs would go in the spring, when the ice went out of the rivers: first down the Little Sioux, then into the big rivers, and down to the jamming piers a few miles above Mokoman.

They wouldn't go all that way by themselves, of course. A crew of rivermen with peaveys and pikepoles and "corks" in their boots would herd them along from river to river, the way cowboys herd cattle on the range.

If the drive hung up in a narrows or at a sharp bend of a river, the drivers, by dint of peavey-power and dynamite, "broke" the jam, often at great risk to their lives in the rush of suddenly released logs. At such a time a man might find it necessary to "ride 'er out"—that is, to keep his balance on a single log as it tore downstream in the midst of a rearing, tearing, grinding maelstrom of sawlogs. At such a time your riverhog, not above heroics, had been

212

known to toss his peavey and hat ashore as mementoes—should he fail to "ride 'er out."

Jams were about the most dramatic thing in a riverman's life—occupationally, that is—and so they were much talked about. In the Mokoman country the most famous jam was that of June, '88, when the booms broke and the piers went out at the boomhouse above Mokoman. All the logs in the St. Pierre went through that time, carrying away all bridges in their path; their ends were "brushed out" like feather dusters as a result of going through the dalles at Jackson.

If the water were low, the rivermen would have to nurse the drive along by means of a system of dams, opening one dam after another and keeping the logs moving in each succeeding surge of water, making every "hatful" count. If a waterfall were encountered, he might have to build a sluiceway through which the logs could be diverted around the fall.

The drive demanded courage, ingenuity, and no small measure of engineering skill—together with the kind of physical hardihood that enabled a man to work in icy water up to his waist all day, sleep in wet blankets at night, and go to work again, if necessary, with nothing but a chew of tobacco for breakfast.

Our drive would start, in the spring, from the Loon where we had our landing. Until the ice was strong enough to carry a load of logs, we made what was called a "high" or "bank" landing. That is, we cut our hauling road along the shore of the lake, where the land was highest, and simply rolled the logs down into the water. Such landings were often used on rivers, where the logs might be rolled out on the ice for 150 feet or more, leaving a channel on the far side of the stream, of course, to facilitate breaking the landing in the spring.

As soon as the ice on Loon Lake was firm, however—which was later than usual in 1907 because of the heavy snowfall—we began to make ice landings. We then drove the hauling sleighs out on the ice—far down the lake at first, so as to avoid hauling over shed bark—and unloaded there. Two men with peaveys broke down the load, loosening the key logs and allowing the others to roll off on both sides of the sleigh; then with canthooks they rolled the logs out for fifteen feet or so, and piled them two or three high.

It was at the landing that the logs were scaled. The scaler went about with his wooden rule and his book encircled by thick rubber bands. He placed his rule against the small end of each log and wrote down the number of board feet in a book, discounting, of course, for rot and crook. Thus he kept a record of exactly how many feet of timber we were putting in from day to day.

At the landing you could see what progress you were making: you could see the logs piling up on the ice—a million feet, two million, four; we hoped to make it six million feet before the ice went out. You could see the logs stretching out on the lake, waiting for the spring freshets to carry them to the hungry saws.

It was from here that the trees went forth, not as the questing trees of Scripture, hopefully on a time; but in sadness and humiliation out of a ravished forest, leaving behind them ruin in the snow and desolation over the hills they had so long made beautiful.

CHAPTER EIGHTEEN

I

W HERE was I again?" inquired the Whiteface Liar.
"You was tellin' about them thirty Greeks," the barn-
boss said. "Or maybe they was Turks."

"They was Greeks," the Liar said pleasantly. "I mind
now. It was about them thirty Greeks and th' thirty little
trunks. Dangdest sight I ever see."

The Liar looked absently at Callahan, the landing man.

"Callahan," he asked, "what year was it now that
Guffey's bulldog swallered yer fishhook with th' beefsteak
on it."

"That," said Callahan, wincing, "that was th' winter of
nineteen ought one."

"Well, I'm speakin' of th' winter afore that one," the
Liar continued, "and Guffey was havin' trouble keepin' a
crew. Guffey was a mean man, and he was always havin'
trouble keepin' a crew. But that winter th' trouble was
special.

"They was road monkeys sky hookin' in Guffey's camp
that winter, and they was flatheads drivin' four horses.
. . . Got so bad there, fin'lly, looked like th' straw-pushes
might have t' work."

The Liar allowed his audience a little time in which to
form some concept of this unheard of state of affairs.

" 'Bout th' start of th' haulin' season," he continued, "Guffey had t' do somethin' drastic. And that he did. He did that. Danged if he didn't disappear fer 'most a week, leavin' th' camp in charge of Beefslew Jackson.

"When he come back, Guffey had them Greeks with him. Yes, sir, Guffey had thirty Greeks with him. Nobody knowed fer sure where he got 'em. Some said they was a man-catcher in Superior corralled 'em. Some said Guffey got 'em out of th' mines up there in Eveleth or Biwabik.

"Anyhow, there they was—thirty Greeks, plain as th' nose on Callahan's face. And them Greeks—" The Liar paused for historical emphasis. "Them Greeks was th' first Greeks that ever went t' work in a loggin' camp.

"And," he added, "far as I knows, they was the last."

"What about them trunks?" the barn-boss inquired doggedly.

"I was jest comin' t' that," the Liar said, with an air of reproof.

"Them Greeks was peculiar little fellers. Guffey had t' put them all together in their own camp, by theirselves— them Greeks and their little trunks—afore they'd go t' work.

"They was thirty trunks, one fer each Greek. They was peculiar trunks, too. I can't exactly say *how* they was peculiar, but they was different from most trunks."

The Liar searched for some descriptive phrase that might help him to convey an image.

"I'd say they was sort of *fancy* trunks," he said. "Everybody was curious 'bout what th' hell was in them. But there wasn't anybody could find out.

216

"Them Greeks was foxy. They was always one of 'em laid up—different one every day. They'd always leave one feller behind in their camp—laid up, he'd say—t' watch them trunks. So nobody ever did find out what was in 'em.

"Well, them Greeks stood with Guffey fer th' rest of th' winter. They wasn't bad loggers, neither. Peculiar fellers, maybe. Couldn't speak English none. Used t' duck under th' table when they et their bread—like they was 'fraid somebody'd grab it away from 'em. But they was good, willin' workers and, once they was educated t' which was th' business end of a canthook, they wasn't bad loggers—considerin'.

"Anyhow, they stood by Guffey ontil camp broke, and fer that th' mean ol' bastard should of been thankful. But not Mike Guffey.

"We was totin' in from th' D. and I. R. that winter—'bout twelve, thirteen miles, I guess—and when camp broke th' Greeks had a problem gettin' their trunks to th' railroad. They didn't expect to have no problem. Guffey toted th' trunks in fer 'em, and I guess they figgered he'd tote 'em out. But them pore Greeks didn't know Mike Guffey.

" 'Sure,' th' old skinflint says, 'sure, I'll tote yer goddamned trunks out fer ye—fer a dollar apiece.'

"Well, them Greeks was quiet little fellers, and they don't say nothin'—just go and talk things over in their camp. Finally one feller comes out and tells Guffey they decided not t' pay th' buck apiece fer haulin' th' trunks.

" 'All right, ye little monkeys!' Mike yells. He was disappointed, I guess, about losin' them thirty dollars. 'All right, then, ye can carry yer frickin' trunks on yer frickin' backs. And I hopes they breaks,' he says.

"But they didn't carry th' trunks on their backs. They was foxy, them Greeks. Guffey was foxy, maybe, but them Greeks was foxier.

"That evenin' they gets some pickle barrels from out behind th' cook-shanty, and some hammers and nails and haywire—they was always plenty of haywire 'round one of Guffey's camps—from the wood-butcher, and we can hear 'em working away in their camp that night like a lot of beavers.

"And in the mornin', danged if they don't have thirty little sleds made out'n them barrel staves. And settin' there on each sled is one of them little trunks.

"Right after breakfast they got their time from Beefslew —Guffey was too mad t' give it t' them—and they starts down th' road. All them thirty Greeks starts down th' road, haulin' their thirty little trunks on their little sleds made out'n pickle barrels."

The Liar knocked the ashes out of his nosewarmer and smiled reflectively.

"Is that all there's to it?" asked the barn-boss.

"Dangedest sight I ever see," mused the Whiteface Liar, ignoring him.

II

For a long time, in a queer, secret sort of way, there had been bad blood between the shanty-boss and the handyman.

218

Whenever the shanty-boss came within earshot of the handy-man, he would mutter out of the side of his mouth:

"Shake 'em up, Pete."

He would say this in a sly, taunting way which, for some reason nobody could fathom, greatly irritated the handy-man.

"Shake 'em up, Pete," he would say, with a knowing grin, and the handy-man would sometimes reply in cold anger, "Some day, Jake, I'm goin' t' level off at ya."

Nobody ever could figure out what the shanty-boss meant by "Shake 'em up, Pete," and the handy-man never leveled off; so everybody lost interest in the feud eventually, except the shanty-boss and the handy-man.

III

You sat there with your trousers down, over an icy peeled spruce log, in a temperature of forty degrees below zero; and that was bad enough when your evacuatory processes were working smoothly and you did not have to remain there until you were numbed with cold.

But when you were not functioning very well, and you had to sit and shiver with every breath turning into a handful of crystals on the air, and a fair part of you naked and exposed to the paralyzing cold—then you sometimes wondered why you had chosen the life of a lumberjack.

Our latrine, or privy, was no place for pleasant meditation. It was a long trench dug into the hillside a hundred feet or so beyond the other camp buildings. Over this trench had been erected a shack-roofed structure of logs, unheated, of course, and but poorly chinked, so that the snow often drifted in and froze upon the pole which served as a seat.

Even when you were well and robust, a trip to the privy was not to be contemplated with pleasure; but when you were indisposed, it was something you dreaded beforehand —and afterwards long remembered.

One night early in January I had gone to bed with a cold and, I suppose, some fever, since my teeth chattered and I shook with the chills beneath my blanket. It was a bitter night, as was every night of that bitter month; and although we had a good fire going in the stove, icy air speared between the logs with every gust of wind. About midnight I knew that I must get up and go to the privy.

I do not know from what deep recesses of the will I finally summoned strength to pull myself out of bed, struggle into my boots and, wrapping a blanket around my head and shoulders, plunge into the sub-zero darkness. I was, I have no doubt, a comic figure as I hurried up the trail to the privy, clutching my grotesque draperies about me, slipping in my haste, and falling once or twice in the pathway. But I did not feel comic. I felt very low and miserable indeed as I huddled in my blanket on the icy rail. There seemed to be something personal and vindictive in the unrelenting fury of the cold. I felt harassed and beaten, there in the lonely darkness; and, in utter misery of spirit, I came very near to weeping. . . .

No one ever complained about the privy. It never occurred to anyone to complain, I guess—just as no one ever grumbled about the vermin in the bunkhouse, or about wet clothes and blankets on the drive.

IV

I was sprinkling some snow on the floor to settle the dust while I swept out the office, when Joe Gachot came in.

"Hi' ya, kid," he said. "Gettin' much nowadays?"

He glanced at Dempsey, who was taking his Sunday afternoon nap, tiptoed over to me and, after some hesitation, said in a low, confidential voice:

"Lis'n, kid—I thought I ought t' warn ya—"

He looked at me in a very serious, even anxious, manner.

"What are you talking about?" I asked, not very affably.

"Ted Gordon," he said. "Ted's on his way over from Tobin."

Gachot looked toward the door, as if he expected him to come in at any moment.

"He's prob'ly loaded and rarin' t' beat th' be-jesus out of somebody," he said, "and I guess it ain't necessary t' say who."

It took me a little while, still, to understand what Gachot was driving at.

"Look, Joe," I said. "Are you trying to say that I—"

"I ain't tryin' t' say *nothin'*," Gachot interrupted hurriedly. "All I'm tellin' ya is Ted's on his way over here, prob'ly borry-eyed and lookin' fer th' bastard that went t' Mokoman with his wife."

I restrained a strong impulse to plant my fist in his pudgy, pig-eyed face.

"Where did you hear that?" I demanded.

"Never mind where I heard it, kid. I'm just tellin' ya—warnin' ya."

He was talking pretty loudly now, almost as if he wanted Dempsey to hear.

"Ted Gordon," he added more quietly, "is one tough son-of-a-bitch."

"You told me that once before."

"Well, I wouldn't fergit it—if I was you."

I had heard about Ted Gordon's toughness. It was quite well known; there were stories about it. There was the story, for instance, about Ted's fight with Buck Boyer on the Point: about how he knocked out Buck's teeth—and when Buck complained, "You broke me teeth," Ted had replied, "Yes, and the next time I'll break your heart."

I can't say that Gachot's news didn't disturb me. It gave me a queer sort of feeling inside, all right—a feeling of outrage, and of things rushing at me too suddenly, and of being sort of cornered in the office there. All of this, mixed up together, and it wasn't pleasant.

"If I was you," Gachot said solicitously, "I'd haul freight out of—"

Dempsey sat up suddenly, with a great snort, in his bunk.

"God stone th' crows!" he bellowed. "What goes on here?"

He was not referring to me, or to Gachot, however; he had been aroused by a sudden racket and commotion outside the office door.

222

CHAPTER NINETEEN

I

*P*RECISELY on Dempsey's last word the door was flung open and a man burst from the bright outdoors into the dimly lit room. He came in with his head low, legs driving, much like a full-back plunging through a line. Several others crowded in the doorway behind him.

The man snapped upright, looking about him in the half light, and swaying a little on his widespread feet.

"Show me this son-of-a-bitch!" he shouted.

Nobody had to explain that this was Ted Gordon. He was built like a welterweight, dressed like a riverman—stagged pants, driving boots, three or four shirts open down his chest. His red hair was in his eyes and there was a little dry foam at the corners of his mouth.

"I'll show ye the door, and I'll thank ye t' get the hell out of it before I pound ye to a pulp," Dempsey said.

He must have moved very fast, despite his two hundred-odd pounds; for at one moment he was getting out of his bunk, and at the next he was lowering over Ted, and I do not recall anything in between.

Dempsey seized Ted's outer shirt in one of his big fists. The smaller man made as if to strike at him, but apparently thought better of it. Instead, he raged at Dempsey with his bloodshot eyes, speechless, like an angry, red-headed boy.

"Gordon," growled Dempsey coldly, "is this yer customary way of enterin' the office of a camp foreman?"

He tightened his grasp on Ted's shirt and glared at him indignantly.

"I'm ashamed of ye, Ted Gordon," he said. "I'm ashamed fer yer old man, God rest his soul. Now git out of here, and if ye have somethin' ye want t' say, come back like a man, now, instead of a goddam bellerin' bull, and we'll talk about it."

He turned Ted around and started him toward the door; he kicked the door shut after him.

There was something comic, I suppose, about the swift and complete denouement of that particular scene, but I did not laugh. I knew there would be another scene directly—and that I, in all probability, would have a part in it.

And in the ensuing moments of silence I suddenly heard myself talking—in a faint, far-away voice that sounded strangely as if it were coming out of Big Bill's gramophone—and yet as plain as though I were in a room alone and talking to myself:

He'll kill you, probably . . . but you'll have to fight him . . . there's nothing else you can do . . . you've got to fight him . . . so get ready. . . .

And I *was* ready—tense, and trembling a little, but ready and not afraid—when, about thirty seconds later, Ted came back. He made his entrance this time with a sort of tipsy dignity, and established himself in the center of the floor. His eyes went around the room until they rested on me; then, ominously, they traveled no farther.

"Well, Ted," Dempsey said, with somewhat exaggerated formality, "what can we do fer ye, now?"

Ted stood stiffly, his fists clenched against his belly, staring at me.

"I come to kill the bastard that took my wife down to Mokoman," he said. "I come to kill your clerk."

"Ted Gordon," Dempsey said softly, "ye're drunk and ye're talkin' like a goddam fool."

"I'll kill him outside," Ted said, "and if the lousy bastard won't come outside, I'll kill him here—and God help anybody tries to stop me."

He was making words in a strange, mechanical sort of way, with long pauses between them.

"Ted Gordon," Dempsey shouted in a suddenly loud voice, "come to yer senses! Who told ye this cockeyed story? Who told ye my clerk took yer wife t' Mokoman?"

Ted's eyes, I observed, shifted to Gachot, who had been standing quietly against the wall. Gachot began to edge toward the door.

"Stand where ye are, Joe," Dempsey said sharply. "Clerk, come here, now."

I placed myself beside him.

"Ted, this is me clerk," Dempsey said. "This is Matt Bradley. Ye mind Jim Bradley—a old friend of yer father's. He was the lad's old man."

Gordon gazed at me stonily.

"Ted," Dempsey said, "the feller told ye the story about him and yer wife going t' town is a liar." He said this very slowly and distinctly; but with still greater emphasis he went on, "That feller is a liar and a son-of-a-bitch, and he ought t' have his heart cut out."

Quite a long silence followed this fearsome pronouncement. I glanced at Gachot. There were drops of sweat on his forehead, and I could guess why.

"Clerk," Dempsey asked, "did Cherry Gordon leave camp with ye that mornin' ye went down?"

"Yes, sir."

"How *far* did she go with ye?"

"She went as far as Panger. She asked if she could go along as far as Panger so she could catch the Dinkey to the Range."

"Do ye hear that, Ted?" Dempsey asked.

"I hear it," Ted said grimly.

Dempsey turned to me again.

"Did anybody see ye and Cherry when ye left camp that mornin'?" he asked.

"Yes, sir. We passed the landing crew just this side of the Wolf," I said.

"Do ye hear that, Ted?"

"Yeah," Ted said. "Yeah, I hear."

"Well," said Dempsey, "they is four men on the landing. They is Tom Mooney . . . and Stokes Allen . . . and Joe Gachot—"

Suddenly Ted lunged at Gachot. Dempsey intercepted him, wrapped his arms around him in a sort of bear-hug.

They swayed and scuffled about the cabin, Ted making muffled, inarticulate sounds punctuated occasionally by loud roars; Dempsey sweating silently in the grim waltz.

226

But it was an altogether unequal struggle, and Dempsey soon had his smaller antagonist pinned against the wall and was methodically banging his head against the logs.

"Listen to me, goddamit!" he bellowed. "Will ye listen, now?"

And, finally, Ted quieted down and listened.

"I'll not have ye brawlin' and fightin' in me office," the boss panted. "That I'll not have, by God!"

He released Ted, who remained standing against the wall, like a boxer against the ropes, his head lowered a little, breathing hard and glaring at Gachot.

"Now," said Dempsey, "git out! Git out—the both of ye!"

"Okay, Pat," Ted said. "I'll get out. I'll be waitin' outside."

He yanked open the door and left. We could hear a hubbub among the men who had gathered in the street during the fracas in the office. Through the open door we could see that the street was filled with men—most of the crew, it appeared. They were standing quietly enough, waiting.

Dempsey hitched his galluses and turned to Gachot, who was standing, silent and sick-looking, in the angle made by my bunk and the wall.

"Well, Joe—" he said.

II

Gachot had sat down on a chair; he tipped it back against the wall, his legs dangling; he looked as though

227

he meant to stay there for a while. Gachot's face was pretty pale, and shiny with perspiration, although it was none too warm in the office.

Dempsey gave him one of those looks from under his eyebrows, and Gachot smiled at him. It was a rather horrible smile, and I almost found myself feeling sorry for Gachot. Dempsey lay down on his bunk again.

The hubbub outside the office kept up, and finally there was a knock at the door.

"Come in," Dempsey called, raising himself up on his elbows.

Paddy MacMahon stepped into the room. Paddy was a sort of spokesman for the crew whenever any collective negotiation with Dempsey was necessary. He was a neat-looking man with sparse gray hair and he possessed a natural charm and suavity, along with the gift of gab. I had once heard Paddy make a moving plea to the boss for permission to play cards in the bunkhouse. At the end of that speech Dempsey had said, "No," but the plea was eloquent, nevertheless.

But this time Paddy did not make a speech. He took off his cap, as was his custom, and addressed the boss respectfully in his agreeable Irish voice.

"Pat," he said, "there is a gent outside would like to speak with Joe."

"Well, there he is, Paddy," Dempsey said, and lay back on his bunk again.

I looked at Gachot, naturally, to see what he would do. He did nothing. He just sat there on his chair, tipped against the wall. I was afraid he would smile again, but he didn't; he just sat there, his face a little pale, and shiny, and expressionless.

Paddy looked at him too, but didn't say anything. He went out, and pretty soon the noise outside increased. Then you could hear Ted shouting.

"Come on out here, you lousy bastard!" he yelled. "Come on out, you lousy bastard! Come on out—"

He began to shout louder and louder, and sometimes he choked and just made fearful sounds. I looked out of the window and saw him standing there, a little in front of the other men, bareheaded and red-faced and crying like a baby.

It became worse and worse. Ted yelled everything he could think of to bring Gachot out.

"Your mother's a whore and you're a son of a whore, and now if you're half a man you'll come out and fight," he raged.

He said worse, much worse, than that; but through it all Gachot sat there against the wall, without a flicker on his livid, porcine face—without a change of expression, except that maybe his eyes seemed to get smaller and smaller.

It grew dark. I lighted the lamps; then the supper horn blew, and it became quieter outside the door. Looking through the window, I could see that the men were breaking away from the group around Ted and drifting toward the cook-shanty. Finally Ted sort of broke down and was led away, sobbing, by some of the others. Then the camp street was silent.

It was silent, too, in the office for a little while; and the silence was stale and sickening, like a stench.

"Well, clerk," Dempsey said. "Better make Joe's time out. Guess he'll be goin' down tonight."

III

"Dominus vobiscum!" Father Donovan's baritone echoed through the cook-shanty and rattled among the pots and tin dishes at the far end of the camp.

"Et cum spiritu tuo." Bullhead Bailey mumbled his responses with the mechanical air of the practiced acolyte.

It was a strange thing to see Bullhead serving Mass. It hardly seemed possible that he was the same individual who, only the day before, had called the shanty-boss a thick-skulled son of a lop-eared, nickel-plated, brass-bellied, monkey-brained bastard and son-of-a-bitch—or something that sounded approximately like that, but was much better.

Bullhead was socalled not because he was stubborn or difficult, but because he somewhat resembled a species of fish known as the bullhead or catfish. With his trailing mustache and flat, receding face, the resemblance was really striking.

Bullhead was not very impressive to look at, nor very edifying to listen to as a general thing; but when he served Mass for Father Donovan he seemed to acquire a certain aloof dignity that was puzzling to the crew of Camp Dempsey.

Father Donovan seldom got around to a camp more

than once during the winter; so his arrival was always an important event, spiritually and, in a sense, socially.

The priest was a small, energetic man with the face of an Irish bantamweight, and with a deep, simple and masculine piety. Like the Sisters, he had the news of the other camps with him; and this news he dispensed willingly and with a sense of humor that was highly appreciated by the men.

In the evening, after supper, Father Donovan set up his confessional in the cook-shanty; and a good many of the crew went in to tell him their sins, sitting contemplatively on the table-benches until it was their turn to go back of the blanket, stretched across a corner of the camp, and confess.

After breakfast next morning Father Donovan said Mass and gave communion. He said his Mass at a little altar he had made out of packing cases, and had covered with the cook's white aprons for an altar-cloth; and not in St. Peter's itself could the Sacrament have been celebrated with greater dignity. For the Mass asks nothing of time or place to strengthen the profound and simple symbolism of its ritual. After the service Joe Lavoie had a special breakfast for Father Donovan and those who had received the Sacrament.

Once or twice during the winter other "skypilots" also visited camp; but in Dempsey's, at least, they never seemed to receive quite the same cordial welcome that was given to Father Donovan. Most of our crew were either Irish Catholic or atheist, with little enthusiasm for evangelical services.

Besides, there was something different about Father Donovan; it was known he'd have a drink with a man, was the cold bad enough, or was there something proper to celebrate. And there usually was.

IV

With the jumper-box full of spare axes and canthooks, it was Dempsey's daily custom to drive about the works like a Roman procurator inspecting his provinces.

"All right, boys!" he would shout, appearing suddenly at a skidway. "Keep things handy around here!" Or, to a straw-push, "How 'bout a little intensive loggin' today, Jim?"

"Here comes th' bull of th' woods," a sawyer would say, spotting his approach, and the crosscuts would ring more briskly, the swampers' axes *thunk* in accelerated rhythm.

"Give 'er snoose, boys!" Dempsey would bellow appreciatively, and the men would grin and put their backs into it.

Like all camp foremen, Dempsey drove his crew. He drove it by profanity, by sarcasm, and, if necessary, by example. He could spot a man riding his saw halfway across a quarter section, and project his remarks about it almost the same distance; he could, and sometimes did, take a peavey from a landing-man and demonstrate the proper way of breaking down a load. By profanity and, if need be, by example, Dempsey spurred his men to greater efforts for the Company. But mostly he did it by wile.

Quite shamelessly, like all other camp foremen, Dempsey took advantage of the logger's naïve, almost pathetic passion to be known as "a good man."

With what cunning did he pit one sawyer against another, skidder against loader, loader against teamster! And with what innocence did the men strive to outdo one another—for no other reward save a grunt of approval, possibly, from the boss, and the esteem of their fellow workers.

It was a driving force so powerful, this artless competitive spirit, that it rang out in the very songs of rivermen and loggers:

"Here's health to Bull Gordon and Kennebec John;
The biggest day's work on the river they done.
So fill up your glasses and fill them up full;
We'll drink to the health of the little brown bulls."

And so, day after day, skidders would strive to catch up with their sawing crews. Loaders would hope to get ahead of hauling teamsters. Sawyers competed with sawyers.

The competition between sawing crews, indeed, was the most spirited of all. Every night the crews turned in their reports on the number of logs cut during the day. Often, when a crew had had a good day and was well ahead of its rivals, it would "bank" ten or fifteen logs, to be turned in on some less successful day. But Dempsey could always tell, in the end, whether or not a sawyer's reports were honest; the scaler's weekly report gave him the official score.

And Dempsey, you may be sure, overlooked no chance

afforded by the weekly reports to spur the sawing crews to greater production.

"Percy," he would say plaintively, after I had read off the figures to him, "Percy, I didn't used t' think Pat Dempsey'd wind up running a old ladies' home."

Dempsey drove his men because he wanted to put in six million feet that winter; and he wanted to do it at a lower cost than any other logger on the St. Pierre. For there was competition among boss loggers too. Pat Dempsey also wanted to be known as "a good man."

V

Big Bill had just come over from Tobin's, out of breath and in great distress.

"I just went out to th' privy," he kept repeating, "and when I come back she was gone."

It was within a couple of hours of darkness, and a west wind with snow behind it was rising. Dempsey looked anxiously at the sky.

"Are ye sure, Bill?" he asked again. "Did ye look everywhere, now? Stop and think, man."

"I tell you, she was sittin' there back of th' stove when I went out to th' privy," Big Bill said. His eyes were pitiful to look into.

"There wasn't nothin' unusual," he said. "She was talkin'—" He stopped, a look of tortured perplexity on his big, kindly face. "She was runnin' on th' way she's been doing sometimes, lately. About greens," Big Bill said. "She was talkin' about greens—said she thought there might be some in th' woods, maybe.

234

"I get kind of tired hearin' about them greens. . . . Maybe that's why I went to th' privy. Maybe that's why—

"Good God, Paddy!" Big Bill cried out suddenly. "Ain't you goin' to help me find Jennie?"

"Now, Bill," Dempsey said, and he put his arm around the big man. "Now Bill, take it easy now. Sure we'll help ye find her."

He stood for a moment watching the wind in the pines.

"Clerk," he said, "git out and find Percy. Tell him t' git th' crew over t' Tobin. Bill and me's startin' right now. Tell Percy t' hurry."

We went into the office, I to get my cap and mackinaw. Dempsey went back of the counter and got out the bottle of John Jameson he kept hidden there. He poured some of the whiskey into a tumbler and handed it to Big Bill.

"Here, Bill," he said, "it'll do ye good."

Big Bill took the drink and held it for a while in his two hands.

"I ain't had a drink for more'n twelve years," he said vacantly. "Jennie won't like this, Paddy."

He tipped the glass up and slowly drank the whiskey.

In the black blizzard that howled down from the west that night, Camp Dempsey's crew worked doggedly over the slashings that circled Tobin. The men kept close together—but a few yards apart—so as to maintain contact with one another. Their teamsters' lanterns bobbed dimly, blacked out, glimmered again in the shrieking darkness as the searchers clambered over deadfalls, stumbled and fell in the great drifts. Foot by foot, they combed the forty lying north of the camp.

Toward midnight they dragged into Jennie's kitchen where Joe Lavoie had coffee on the stove and food on the table. They sat heavily in pools of melted snow, gulping coffee and talking dejectedly about the hunt.

"I don't think she could of got any farther than we went through th' slashings," Phil Leonard said. "I think we ought t' try th' swamp next."

"Why would she want t' get into them swamps?" asked the handy-man.

"Why would she want—?" Leonard looked at the handy-man in weary disgust.

"We're goin' to take a turn over th' ridge," one of the Galloping Twins said. "We got a hunch."

"You're goin' where I goddam tell ye to go," Dempsey said. "We'll try the stretch betwixt here and th' crick."

Through the talk, Big Bill sat at the head of the table, his hands around a cup of cold coffee, listening dully.

All night long the search went on, and when at last the dawn broke clear and crimson across the stilled snows, it was I who found poor Jennie.

I found her hardly thirty paces from her kitchen door, in a space where the wind had scooped the snow up and uncovered a patch of her blue house dress. She wore one of Big Bill's frayed jackets over the dress, and that is all; she must have frozen very quickly.

Beside her in the snow we found a basket and a shovel with which the wood ashes were taken from the kitchen range.

"Looks like she come out t' *dig* fer somethin'," said the barn-boss. "Danged if *I* can cypher *that* out."

236

CHAPTER TWENTY

I

*T*oward the end of March the bears began to get into the garbage back of the cook-shanty, but we didn't need them to tell us that spring was at hand and the hauling season about over.

The thaws began during the last week of the month, and it was apparent that we would have to do, in Dempsey's words, some pretty "intensive logging," if we were to get the cut in before the ice rotted on the roads. Dempsey figured we could make it by April third—which was an extraordinarily late date.

As that day approached a great restlessness agitated the crew—like that which seizes troops too long in camp. In the bunkhouse the interminable discussions of women and liquor grew more and more animated, more colorful and richer in detail, as anticipation neared the real thing.

"Their tongues is hangin' out as long as seven clotheslines," said Dempsey.

Finally a few of the men—the weaker-willed or, possibly, merely the more imaginative—could stand the strain no longer and went down several days before the break-up.

There was a great increase, too, in "boiling up," as the

men prepared for the return to town. The shanty-boss did a thriving business in trimming hair and beards, and some of the men contemplated shaving. So pervasive was the spirit of "sprucing up" that even the bull-cook was observed regarding himself—with some astonishment, it appeared—in the bunkhouse looking glass.

In other, less patent ways, too, the approach of the long winter's end affected the spirits and actions of the men. Some became irritable, some ebullient—some morose, as though conscious of the futility of the life they led.

More and more frequently, I noticed, the married men showed me their worn photographs—often pasted in the hunting case of a watch—of wives and families. Some of these men gathered little bags of spruce gum to take to their children. Some asked me to write letters for them, saying they would soon be home.

During the last week we began to haul at night, when the roads were more solid. There was no moon and the work was hard and dangerous in the darkness, lit only by our vinegar-jar lanterns. But the weather was deteriorating rapidly. We carried snow from the deep woods in sugar barrels and shoveled it into the ruts; and it was nip and tuck, during those closing days, whether we would finish hauling before the roads broke down completely.

On the second of April, however, the cook started to pack up, so that he would be ready to move early next morning. The blacksmith and handy-man were also prepared to leave. Even the men had packed their turkeys and some were planning to start at midnight—as soon as I could make out their time.

An air of almost unbearable suspense hung over the whole camp. It was like the night before Christmas in a house full of children.

II

Big Bill came over several days before we broke camp. We hadn't seen him since he went down to Mokoman for Jennie's funeral, and he looked bad. It was shocking to see how his big, amiable face had sagged; and you knew without smelling his breath that something besides grief had dulled and reddened his eyes.

"Sad t' see you all movin' on," Bill said.

He had come in while I was in the midst of packing up the wannigan.

"Want some help, lad?" he asked.

"No, thanks," I said. "I know where everything goes."

Big Bill leaned far across the counter and scrutinized the empty shelves below—in the neighborhood of the place where Dempsey kept the John Jameson.

"Paddy still got that bottle cached away?" he asked.

He put on a great show of casualness, but when I looked up I noticed, for the first time, that his hands were shaking badly.

"Guess he has," I replied, honestly but with a sad lack of common sense.

Big Bill's nervousness increased visibly. He dropped his voice very low and said with a wink, "How 'bout a little snort, clerk?"

"Sorry, Bill," I told him. "Dempsey keeps it locked up, and he's got the key."

"Oh," Bill said. "Just thought we might have one t' celebrate."

He said no more about the liquor until, about an hour before supper time, Dempsey came in. The boss, I could see, was also shocked by Bill's appearance. The talk between them, I noticed, had a strange, strained quality, for conversation between such old friends. Presently Bill asked, "Anything left in that bottle, Paddy?"

Dempsey said nothing for a long, nervous minute or so. Then—

"Bill," he said in a flat, weary voice, "ye have been drinkin'."

"I have not, Paddy."

"No need t' deny it, Bill. Ye are drinkin'."

"Only a drop," Bill said. "Only a drop at th' wake, Paddy."

His face twitched and he tried pitifully to avoid Dempsey's eyes.

"Maybe," he suggested hopefully, "maybe we should all have a little drink, howsoever—on th' completion of a successful season."

Then, in the aching silence, a hoarse whisper from a desperate man—"For th' love of Christ, Paddy—can't ye give me a drink?"

Dempsey got heavily to his feet, unlocked the cupboard where the whiskey was kept, and handed the half-filled bottle to Big Bill. He handed Big Bill the bottle, then turned away and stood looking out of the window into the making dusk.

"God stone th' crows!" he said. "Ain't we never goin' t' get no supper?"

III

As spring drew near—spring and the time when the ice on the hauling roads would give out and, the winter's cut in, the camps would break—I found excuses for going to Panger; and on almost every trip I contrived to see Sari.

Sometimes I merely stopped in for a cup of coffee. Once I happened by just as Sari and her father had taken their baths and the stones in the *sauna* were still hot. So we put more wood on the fire and I also bathed.

"When you have finished your bath," Sari said, before I went into the *sauna*, "throw the *vasta* between your legs."

"The *vasta?*"

"Yes, the little switch you beat yourself with."

"Why should I do that?"

"Oh, just do it," Sari laughed. "And then notice which way it points."

One, of course, should never bathe alone in a *sauna,* for how can one properly belabor oneself with the little bundles of cedar, let alone converse with oneself—and what is a *sauna* without sociability!

But I made out tolerably well. I poured a little water on the hot field stones and sat on the second step of the three-tiered bench, and perspired in streams and rivulets as the hot vapor filled the little room; and, when I became used to the heat—which I feared at first would sear my lungs—I moved up to the highest seat, where it was even more intense and I perspired even more profusely.

Then I soaped myself well with a bar of yellow soap and hot water from a bucket and, as best I could, beat myself crimson with the *vasta*. The sweet aromatic smell of the cedar mingled with the odor of sweat and steam, burning rocks, and wood fire smoke, and gave a *sauna*-smell, which is different from any other in the world.

Only because Sari assured me that she also did it—and how could I confess myself less courageous than a girl?—I emptied the bucket of ice cold water over my head at the end. And so, having survived this last rigorous ritual of the *sauna* successfully, I emerged from the little bath-house at least four shades whiter, and ravenous for the coffee and *limppu* which Sari had ready.

"Did you do as I told you with the *vasta?*" Sari asked.

"Yes," I said. "And now—"

"Which way did it point?"

"It pointed this way—toward the house."

Sari laughed gaily; and I thought there was a sort of happy confusion in her laugh.

"Why? What does it mean?" I insisted.

"Oh, nothing," Sari said. "It doesn't mean anything, really."

And so, for the time being, I remained in ignorance of an old Finnish superstition that if a boy throws the *vasta* between his legs in the *sauna,* it will point in the direction from which his sweetheart is to come.

242

Once on a Sunday I found time to go with Sari over her trap lines, the string of small steel traps she had set for mink and marten along the lower Wolf. And on one particular Sunday—it was Easter and the last Sunday I was to spend in Camp Dempsey—we went for a sort of holiday jaunt on skiis.

It was not a very long trip, merely to Garnet Lake, which lay several miles northeast of the Luomala homestead. Garnet was a small but very lovely lake, surrounded by a fine stand of pine, which came down close to the water's edge—or, I should say, the ice's edge—without the usual alder thickets along the shore. Under the high ceiling of the pines (they must have reached fifty feet to the nearest branches) there was a complete absence of underbrush: there was nothing but the smooth, shadowy snow.

The forest, it is true, is never absolutely silent, never perfectly quiet. Even on the stillest day, there is movement in the restless crowns of the pines, a stir of life in the living organism of the woods. And yet, on that day there was no sound that you would have been conscious of, except the thin *cre-e-p* of our skiis across the snow.

As we penetrated deeper into the forest, Sari, who loved so much to talk, became silent too. We stopped to watch a handful of snow fall from a lofty branch, a glittering, rosy shower in the almost horizontal rays of the late sun.

"Matt," Sari said after a while, "can you feel the woods?"

Her voice, as she spoke, had that peculiar littleness and remoteness that voices have in a winter forest.

"I mean the way you would feel pain, or happiness,

or grief. It's something *inside* you—very strong and sharp —I—I can't explain. . . ." She stopped abruptly.

"You're laughing at me, Matt," she said.

"No, I'm not," I protested, seriously. "Go on."

"Well— I think it must be something very, very old. Like the fear some people have of the dark—and things in the night. Maybe it's so old that most people have lost it at last. Children have it more than grown-ups. I think most of us Finns still have it. . . ."

"It sounds sort of—sort of frightening."

"It is," Sari agreed. "Beautiful, but frightening, too. That's why I think it must be so old—something from the time when people were always afraid."

She smiled a strange, apologetic little smile.

"Have you ever been on the ocean?" she asked.

"No," I said.

"Well, I think it must be something like that—like being out in the middle of the empty sea. Or in a great, silent cave. Or—" She glanced at me in exactly the way children sometimes do when they suspect they are not being taken seriously. "Or—as if you saw a fiery volcano making the sky red at night.

"It isn't what you *see*," she said, "or what you *hear*. It's all what you *feel*. You could be blind and deaf— it wouldn't matter. It might even help—close your eyes and see."

I obligingly closed my eyes, but it was unnecessary. For how could one be insensitive, even if one had wished, to the ancient spell of that great dark forest? How could one escape those deep stirrings of lost instincts: those faint echoes from the prehistoric past—the strongest and most moving of all man's memories, perhaps, because they must be the oldest?

"I know what you mean," I said. "You don't have to be a Finn."

"No, you don't," Sari laughed. "But it helps."

It was dark and moonless during the last hour of our return; but March, like August, is a month of northern lights, and they were trembling now like wind-stirred incandescent draperies, moving like falling playing cards of light, shifting restlessly in vast and silent maneuverings of cold, polar color above the hilltops to the north.

And then they were all around us. A white ground mist had gathered in the valley where the Luomala farmstead lay and, as we walked down into it, we were enveloped by chilling clouds of silvery vapor through which *aurora borealis* moved across the earth. The strange light played through the mist in churning, kaleidoscopic patterns of pale color. We moved through an eerie world, lighted by frozen flames that seemed to run and flicker all about us. It was something that neither Sari nor I had ever before experienced, and we went slowly and silently on our skiis along the Corey-Nixon road, in that awesome night.

It was too late to stop for coffee, so I said good-by to Sari at the cabin door. She pulled off her mitten and smiled up at me as she held out her hand. But it was not her usual quick, happy smile; it came slowly, and I sensed something abstracted and remote in her manner, almost as if the strangeness of the night had overcast her gay spirit. And her eyes, extraordinarily large and dark in the misty light of the restless sky, seemed to look past me, even while they met mine.

"Well, good-by, Matt," she said, giving my hand a tight little squeeze. *"Hyvästi."*

"Sari," I said, stumbling awkwardly over what I wanted to say, "Sari, I wish—I hope—"

"So do I, Matt," said Sari. "I want to see you again too. I'm coming to Mokoman in June. I'm coming, sure—to visit Lyyli. We'll see each other then."

We stood for a while longer, talking absently about Sari's visit to Mokoman. We promised to write to each other, and we discussed Joe Panger's erratic handling of the mails. We laughed about that in a way that was a little forced and a little nervous; we searched for other things to talk about.

Then, quite abruptly, as if another voice had joined in the conversation, I heard myself say, "I'm glad I found you, Sari—at last."

Sari laughed, this time gaily.

"I said that first. That time in Panger. I said I was glad we had met, finally."

"I was too. I wanted to tell you. But I guess I was too—surprised."

"That I wasn't an Indian?"

"Well—yes."

"Were you disappointed?"

"Yes."

It was one of those small private jokes that people have

246

between them—people who are close to each other. We laughed once more, then stood silent for a little while.

"Anyhow," Sari said, "we've had lots of fun together, haven't we?"

She looked up at me happily.

"I always feel *good* when I'm with you, Matt."

"That's the way—" I began.

Then, quite as naturally and simply as I had taken her small hand to say good-by, I pulled Sari close to me and kissed her, and the touch of her lips was warm and firm against mine. . . .

Dempsey's gray, eager as always to get back to his stall, pounded down the Corey-Nixon road. We came up out of the mist-filled valley and into the clear, cold, wonder-shot night. Through the ghostly slashings we lurched along—an old horse, a crude sleigh, a boy—and so made our way back to Dempsey's, on a night that was, of all nights, God's most wonderful.

CHAPTER TWENTY-ONE

I

WHILE Dempsey and the scaler snored in their bunks, I worked through the night, making out the men's time checks.

I was not "handy with figures" and, even though I had done as much as possible beforehand, the task was a physical and nervous strain—as any all-night press of work is likely to be. But there was no alternative. The last log was in, and camp was breaking immediately after breakfast in the morning.

Some of the men, so eager were they to get to town, left at midnight. I paid them off and, with their turkeys on their backs, they stepped out briskly in the chill darkness of the moonless night, hoping to make Mokoman by the next evening.

The teamsters and their horses took the river route back, trudging along in the slush which covered the ice. Some of the teams drew sleighs loaded with camp equipment: surplus provisions, harness, blankets, the wannigan, left-over feed and hay, and articles requiring repair or replacement before Dempsey's camp could begin another logging season. The other horses were hitched together in long files, the drivers riding one of the lead horses.

The men took the shorter route, by way of the tote-roads over which I had come to Tobin so long ago—so very long ago, it seemed to me. They started down immediately after breakfast, just as day was breaking. They left quietly, in little groups, some after shaking hands with Dempsey, most of them without farewells of any kind.

Many of the married men would presently be at work in the sawmills and lumber yards—loaders into carriage men, swampers into pilers. The mills, according to reports, would be in operation by the tenth. The ice in the St. Pierre, the *Pine Torch* said, was already rotten; the snow was on the run in Mokoman, with garbage piles once more appearing along the roadsides. In town, as well as in the woods, winter was drawing at last to its long close, and soon the drone of the mills, the piney fragrance of the yards, would fill the summer air in Mokoman.

Among the single men there were many who—after an interlude on the Point, of course—would return to the woods for the drive. Around the first of May, the driving crews would begin to herd the logs, cut by a score or more of camps during the winter, down the river courses to the mills. The drives, quite probably, would be over by the middle of July; then back to the woods to work on the "dry rear" until August had run half its course. Another interlude, the woods again: that was the rhythm of life for shanty boy and river hog; that was the pattern of their years.

The last man out of camp that morning, and by design, I suspect, was Jake McCloskey. At the edge of the timber he faced about, opened his great mouth and emitted the same yawp that had announced his arrival in December. The echoes of his yells died away in the pines. The silence of desertion enveloped Dempsey's camp.

The bunkhouse, suddenly, seemed vast again, and incredibly still, the bunks stripped, the stoves cold: an enormous living room empty of every sign of life, save the gnawing of a rat somewhere beneath the floor. The cook-shanty, once the center of warmth and comfort, was even more unnatural in its chill barrenness. Without its men, its horses, its friendly fires, the whole camp had a strange and unfamiliar look: strange and unbelievable, like the corpse of little Jo-jo Poquette when he was killed so suddenly in the woods.

Those of us who had been left behind went about our tasks a little sadly, I think. Several men with a team of horses pulled the hauling sleighs up on small skids, to keep the runners off the ground, stacking them several bobs high. I packed up the camp books and a few odds and ends of wannigan, tobacco mostly, which had not gone down that morning.

Dempsey took the jumper and, without spare axes or canthooks this time, drove over "the works," perhaps to make sure that no equipment had been left lying about in the woods. The Galloping Twins moved into the office with the boss and me; they were to remain behind as camp watchers through the summer.

In the morning we too would leave for town. On the afternoon before our departure I climbed the ridge, where the tote-road dipped down the hill, and from which I had first seen Dempsey's camps whole and complete in early winter. I wanted another look, a last look at the little knot of buildings which, for almost half a year, had been my world.

III

Even at that distance it was not the same. Even in the soft saffron light of an April afternoon, Dempsey's camp no longer had the trim, clean look of a model in some museum—a model with cotton on its roofs, and everything neat and tidy.

The snow was gray and dirty now, and where it had melted, the winter's ugly accumulation of debris had been exposed. No smoke rose from its chimneys; no life stirred in the low log buildings. And the new spring green of the willows, bursting into furry catkins along the Wolf, seemed only to accentuate the dishevelment, one might almost say the desolation, that had fallen on Dempsey's camp.

And yet, if you viewed it in a practical way, with a logger's eye—the way old Alec Mackenzie, for instance, would have seen it—you could tell without looking twice that it was a snug, tight set of camps, solidly built and properly laid out. It had been a well-found camp, too, and an efficient one; for we had put in our six million feet of pine as planned, and some to boot. And, all in all, it had been a happy camp, as Dempsey's usually was.

Many things, both good and bad, had happened there, as you would have expected, in the hundred and twenty days we had been up for Dempsey. To the Keelers—poor Jennie and Big Bill, and Cherry Gordon too—bad and pitiful things. To myself—and this I knew suddenly and strongly as I looked down on the sun-warmed roofs of Dempsey's abandoned camps—to myself something good: something right and proper to a young man; and this I felt simply and surely within myself, as tangibly and solidly as the feel of strong, fit muscles.

Solid and tangible now, at the winter's end, was the knowledge that I had taken my father's place in our family; that I had acquitted myself with credit among tough and exacting men; that I had faced tragedy and overcome despair as a man should and must.

And less simply—with an almost mystical perception— I sensed inside myself a new strength and readiness against my future. Now I knew surely that I should not come back to the woods winter after winter, as had my father; that the sawmills and logging camps of Mokoman would not wear me out as they did most of Mokoman's men; that somehow I should return to college, if not the next fall, then another, as my mother dreamed and believed I would.

I knew surely now that the limits of Mokoman were not needfully the boundaries of my own world. And all the things I had with some deep instinct put store by—in a groping, uncertain, lonely way—I knew that my feeling about them was not a feeling improper to a man. That it was not unmanly, as so many in Mokoman held, to be stirred by beauty and wonder; to love books and to hunger for knowledge—even useless, impractical knowledge of obscure and distant places, and long-dead men and women; or to respect things strange and unaccustomed. That such things were nothing for a grown man to be ashamed of and cast away with his youth, but something to keep and live by.

And so, quite suddenly, doubts and uncertainties that had troubled me no little through the long winter melted away like the snow on Dempsey's camps. By what warmth I did not trouble to question; but all at once, more than anything else, I wanted to talk about it to Sari.

"I won't be going down with you in the morning," I told Dempsey that evening. "I'm going over to Panger."

Dempsey grinned and shook hands with me. I guess he knew about Sari.

"Well, good luck to ye, lad," he said. "Ye have been a good clerk. Ye ain't a bad one in th' woods neither. I have watched ye spellin' th' swampers. I'd say ye are a good man with an ax—save yer grip's a leedle tight, maybe."

He gave me one of those up-slanting looks from under his bushy eyebrows.

"They's a lot ye can learn in th' woods that them professors can't learn ye," he said.

He beamed at me with an air of proprietorship, just as he had that night so long ago, it seemed, in McKinnon's saloon.

"I'd say ye have learned to cypher," said Dempsey.

Other books written by Walter O'Meara

The Trees Went Forth
Tales of the Two Borders
The Grand Portage
Minnesota Gothic
The Spanish Bride
The Savage Country
The First Northwest Portage
The Last Portage
The Devil's Cross
Guns at the Forks
Just Looking
The Duke of War
Daughters of the Country
The Sioux Are Coming!